A BRIEF HISTORY OF
SCIENCE
WITH LEVITY

A BRIEF HISTORY OF
SCIENCE
WITH LEVITY

THE APPROPRIATION AND MANIPULATION
OF SCIENCE AND TECHNOLOGY

MIKE BENNETT

Matador
9 Priory Business Park
Kibworth Beauchamp
Leicestershire LE8 0RX, UK
Tel: (+44) 116 279 2299
Email: books@troubador.co.uk
Web: www.troubador.co.uk/matador

ISBN 978 1784622 954

British Library Cataloguing in Publication Data.
A catalogue record for this book is available from the British Library.

Printed and bound in the UK by TJ International, Padstow, Cornwall
Typeset in Calibri by Troubador Publishing Ltd

Matador is an imprint of Troubador Publishing Ltd

In memory of my sister Alison, who died earlier this year.

Also dedicated to my children Dan, Jonny and Tina. I hope that I have encouraged them to follow their dreams as they progress through life.

AUTHOR'S NOTE

The information presented in this book is factual. In cases where the information is inferred or taken from third-party accounts this is stated. In some cases where the information presented comes from confidential sources or individuals who do not wish to be identified, their names have been changed.

INTRODUCTION

The author is an honours physics graduate, engineer and successful entrepreneur.

He has decades of experience interacting with global industrial groups, and the intelligence-security services worldwide. In addition to presenting a history of science and technology, the book relates these experiences with a considerable amount of levity.

As the book progresses it becomes ever more intriguing, starting to explore the interaction between the giant industrial-military corporations and the intelligence-security services. A great amount of information in these areas is disclosed which has hitherto been unpublished.

The author has had long conversations with many people, ranging from leading politicians, diplomats, billionaire heads of industry and security agents from many countries, to beggars, thieves and leaders of rogue nations. With few exceptions, he finds that you can learn a lot from most people if you take the time to listen to them.

For one of the first examples of the appropriation and manipulation of ground-breaking science and technology by the intelligence community, look no further than Wernher von Braun. When he was taken to the USA in 1945, the Americans also took Wehrmacht (Army) General Walter Dornberger, who they claimed was Wernher von Braun's boss. This was pure window-dressing for American public consumption. US intelligence knew full well that Von Braun was a Major in the SS, although this was never disclosed at the time. He had used slave labour from concentration camps to build his V2 rockets. Von Braun actually reported directly to SS General Hans Kammler.

Kammler held the third highest position in the SS, but the Americans knew that the truth would not go down well with the powerful Jewish lobby in Washington.

Kammler's achievements and the towering advances made by his group of scientists and engineers were truly ground-breaking, and the security system that he put in place to surround and protect these operations was never broken. This model was the start of black project operations, and has been copied by almost all nations ever since.

I ask the readers to set aside any preconceptions they may have regarding science and technology, and to examine the facts presented in this book with an open mind.

PROLOGUE

It was a cold grey Saturday morning in the winter of 1965. I was sitting looking out of the window at the occasional flurries of snowflakes swirling around the building. I was wondering if my parents would let me go fishing with my friends tomorrow.

Suddenly I felt a sharp blow to the side of my head. Our Latin teacher, Mr Bullock, had just thrown the blackboard eraser at me. Yes, I was still in the classroom and my thoughts of fishing would have to wait until later in the day. I was made to go to the board, and write down all of the grammatical cases for "boy" in Latin. There are nominative, vocative, accusative, genitive, dative and ablative in both the singular and plural. Twelve different cases for the word "boy". Does anyone really want to learn this language? To make it worse, nobody today even speaks Latin apart from the Catholic clergy and a few obscure scholars.

I was nine years old at the time, but the influences I had during those early years probably shaped my life.

I had an older sister. We got on fine together, although she normally got the better of me in family disputes, probably because she was older than me. I also have a younger brother who shared many of my interests. I nicknamed him Woolley as he was born in the autumn of 1962, and the UK had the biggest freeze in living memory the following winter.

My mother did her best to care for us all. In those days there was not much money about. She worked very hard, getting up to light the coal stove an hour before she could start cooking breakfast for us all. I learned how to cook by helping her in the kitchen after school.

My father was a government scientist. He did his best to bring us up well, and to give us a good education. Apart for the fee-charging schools, the best school in the area was Bristol grammar school. Provided that you passed the entrance exam, you had access to a good free education. I enrolled in their junior prep school at the age of seven. At the time, I was rather jealous of my friends at our local school, as I had to attend school on Saturday mornings while they enjoyed a two-day weekend.

During the week, I took a bus to school, but on Saturdays my dad drove me to school and went shopping while he was waiting to collect me at lunchtime.

My lifetime interest in both pure science and engineering was sparked at this time. After my dad picked me up from school, we would trawl through army surplus stores, which were common in those days, selling off supposedly obsolete military supplies left over after World War II. We would spend hours looking through shelves filled with parts of old communications equipment, safety equipment and anything else that was no longer considered useful by the armed forces. I was planning to build my first radio receiver, and had taken a book from the local library which contained various circuit diagrams. I think that I became interested in electronics when I wondered what was inside a TV. One day I dismantled our family TV for a look, and put it back together before anyone came home. It didn't work after that, and suffice to say I was grounded (not in the electrical sense of the word).

I needed three particular valves for my radio; two diodes and a triode. For the younger readers, valves, which the Americans call tubes, are hot cathode vacuum devices that were used for electronic switching and amplification prior to the introduction of semiconductors. How things have changed. When I was designing electronic control equipment thirty years later, I used IGBTs (Insulated Gate Bipolar Transistors). They were attached to the largest heat sinks I could find due to the amount of power that they were controlling. In 1965 I never dreamt that such a device could ever be built.

I eventually found the valves I needed, and bought the whole chassis complete with many resistors and capacitors. The following weekend I found an old variable condenser and a small loudspeaker, and I was ready to start. I cut down and riveted the chassis, wired and soldered in all the parts that were needed, and mounted it all in a small wooden box.

In the evenings after my bedtime, I would run a copper wire up to the opposite corner of my bedroom for an antenna, and listen to Radio Luxembourg. It was very comforting to listen to their DJs while looking at the soft orange light coming from the valves in my radio.

My next project was to build a solid-state radio using "modern" transistors. My dad showed me how to etch copper-backed board with ferric chloride, and using two Mullard OC71 transistors with some other parts I soon had my first portable radio.

My dad did very well from the army surplus stores. He bought an old WWII aviator's emergency battery with an orange head cap and light for three shillings and sixpence, which is 17.5 pence in modern money. These batteries were automatically switched on by seawater and were used to help Air Sea Rescue locate airmen ditched in the sea. Airmen were much more valuable than their aircraft, and the use of silver in the batteries was more than justified. At home he cut it up, and discovered that it was full of silver compound and magnesium plates. The MOD quartermasters obviously had no idea of the true value of these batteries.

After that we purchased every battery that we could find. He then sold the silver chloride plates to Johnson Matthey for around £4,000. That was big money in those days, as our five-bedroom semidetached home cost £3,100.

In the evenings he also had us going through bags of silver coins to look for ones that were minted before 1947. The melt value of the silver in these coins was much higher than the face value. The same applies to old American half-dollar coins and others, but I think that they will all have been taken by now.

Although my father worked as a government scientist, I think that it was his entrepreneurial activities that encouraged me to start my own business after I gained enough experience in my working career.

He grew up during WWII, and even after the war you would still not be allowed to enter Oxford or Cambridge universities without having studied Latin. He studied at Imperial College London, and was one of their youngest students ever to be awarded a doctorate. I think that I am lucky to be here today. One day when he was cycling to school a V2 rocket impacted a field about a mile away. On this occasion it only killed a few cows.

Apart from my interest in how things work and general engineering, I have also been fascinated by physics. After completing the core courses required in high school, I chose to study physics, pure mathematics and applied mathematics for my advanced grades. For me, subjects such as languages, geography and others may be very interesting to some, but they are not rapidly evolving at the cutting edge of knowledge.

I, along with the rest of the world, think that the pioneering work of Sir Isaac Newton and Albert Einstein was pure genius. One person that I consider should be up there with them is Nikola Tesla. He was also a ground-breaking genius, but I will elaborate on his achievements in later chapters.

One of my sons is now studying for a masters' degree in physics at the University of Aberdeen. Physics is evolving so rapidly that when we speak, it is clear that many of the things that I was taught at university thirty-five years ago are now known to be incorrect. I was simply taught the best understanding that we had of physics at that time.

I hope that as the reader progresses through this book, he or she will be as captivated by modern science and engineering as I am. I would like to ask the reader to keep an open mind about the issues discussed, and draw their own conclusions from the facts presented.

CHAPTER I

Before going further, I am including a chapter covering some of the basic scientific fundamentals of both physics and chemistry. This is necessary as later in the book we will discuss both the design and application of many advances in detail.

If the reader is an honours chemistry graduate or a recent honours physics graduate, you may wish to skip the next few pages as I am not trying to teach my grandmother how to suck eggs. However I hope that this chapter will be of interest to readers who do not come from a scientific background, and I hope that the brief synopsis in this chapter will help with the understanding of the concepts discussed.

In addition, if the reader is a high school student who happened to miss school when these basics were being taught, I hope that this chapter will help you. Once you have a firm grasp of the essential basics in most subjects, the rest tends to fall into place more easily.

Many centuries ago, philosophers believed that the world around us was formed from four things. They were water, earth, air and fire. As the centuries progressed and science was born, people discovered new materials that were unknown to their ancestors. For example, the end of the Stone Age was marked by the point at which humans discovered bronze. This was a material that they had never before encountered, and they used it to produce new tools and weapons. Although bronze is not an element but an alloy formed mostly from the elements copper and tin, its discovery made people start to question the ideas of the ancient philosophers.

Similarly, the Bronze Age was succeeded by the Iron Age when people discovered that certain rocks, which we now know as ores, could produce other materials when heated. It was obvious to them that the new material, iron, was different from bronze due to its different colour and physical properties.

In more recent times, the early scientists that we now refer to as alchemists started to define the first elements in what we now know as the periodic table of elements. As time progressed, more and more elements were discovered and these elements are today the basis of all chemistry.

An element is defined by the number of protons in the atomic nucleus. For example, if an atom has only one proton in the nucleus it is hydrogen. If it has two protons in its nucleus it is helium, and with three it is lithium and so on. Apart from the most common form of hydrogen, all atoms also have particles called neutrons in their atomic nuclei.

Although hydrogen normally contains a nucleus consisting of just a single proton, hydrogen isotopes also occur that can possess either one or two neutrons within their nuclei. These isotopes are known as deuterium and tritium respectively. Although they are chemically still hydrogen, their nuclear make-up gives them slightly different properties. It is not possible for hydrogen to exist with three neutrons in the nucleus. Tritium is already radioactive and a hydrogen nucleus of this atomic weight cannot accept any further neutrons.

Neutrons are very similar to protons, except that they have no overall electrical charge. A proton has a charge of +1. Neutrons and protons are both made up from subatomic particles known as quarks. Six types of quarks are currently known to science. Physicists normally group them into three pairs, known as the up/down pair, the charm/strange pair, and the top/bottom pair. Associated with each of these quarks, there is also a corresponding antiquark. Quarks also carry another type of charge known as a colour charge, however the discussion of this is beyond the requirements of basic scientific fundamentals.

Quarks are unusual in that they carry a fractional electrical charge. Electrical charge in physics and chemistry is measured against the electrical charge of a proton which is +1. All quarks currently discovered have an electrical charge of either +2/3, or -1/3. Neutrons and protons are each made up of three quarks. Quantum physics dictates that three quarks with the same charge cannot exist together. So for example, if two up quarks (which each have a charge of +2/3) combine with one down quark (which has a charge of -1/3), the resulting particle will be a proton as the overall charge will be +1. Conversely, should one up quark combine with two down quarks, the resulting particle will have an overall charge of zero, and will therefore form a neutron.

As we move away from hydrogen and towards the heavier elements with higher atomic numbers, we find that they contain a varying number of neutrons within their nuclei. These are called isotopes. Isotopes are variants of the same element, but with different atomic weights due to the different number of neutrons within their nuclei. Many of these isotopes are unstable, and throw out particles and electromagnetic pulses from their nuclei, changing them into different isotopes or elements. This is known as radioactivity, and this also needs to be discussed in order to understand how some science has developed when we look at this in detail later in the book.

Radioactivity, or more correctly radioactive decay, is broadly grouped into three categories. These are known as Alpha, Beta and Gamma decay. All three decay modes produce ionising radiation which is damaging to plant and animal life.

Alpha particles are helium nuclei. This means that an alpha particle consists of two protons and two neutrons, but with no surrounding electron shells. They have a relatively short range in air and can easily be blocked by something as simple as a sheet of Perspex.

However, they are hazardous to humans, as they are known as bone seekers. This means that if one inhales air containing alpha particles, they will be absorbed into the body through the lungs and make their way predominantly into the bone marrow. As the bone marrow controls blood cell production, the ionising radiation from the alpha particles will damage the bone marrow and hence the blood cells that it helps to produce. This usually ends with the person contracting leukaemia or some other type of cancer.

Beta particles are high-energy electrons. They also have a relatively short range in air, and can again be blocked by using relatively thin shielding materials. They are also hazardous, as if they are sufficiently energetic they have the capacity to ionise the materials within our bodies, again causing permanent damage.

The third broad category is gamma decay. Gamma rays are very high-frequency energetic electromagnetic waves. They are extremely penetrating and are very difficult to shield against. Depending on the energy of the gamma emissions, as a rule of thumb it takes around one inch of solid lead shielding to attenuate the received gamma ray dose rate by one order of magnitude. This means that powerful gamma ray sources need very thick and heavy shielding in order to get the dose rates on the outside of the shielding down to acceptable levels.

Gamma rays are not absorbed into the body, but pass straight through it, striking our molecules on the way. As you know, humans are made up mostly of water which is H_2O. Gamma rays are capable of splitting a water molecule into free radicals. This means that free hydrogen and oxygen atoms will be produced. These will then recombine, but not necessarily back into water. A free radical of oxygen can combine with an existing water molecule within the body to produce H_2O_2 (hydrogen peroxide), which is toxic.

In addition to the creation of toxic substances within our bodies, long-term damage can be caused when radiation strikes our DNA chains. As the reader will know, DNA is the biological blueprint of how the various cells within the body are constructed. As a good deal of the tissue within the body is continually being regenerated, the damaged DNA chains can cause cancerous tissues to grow. This long-term effect of radiation can result in people developing many types of cancer years after they were actually exposed to the radiation.

One of the key components used in some exotic science today is an isotope known as sodium 22. Sodium is a member of the alkali metals group, and is therefore highly reactive. There are twenty known isotopes of sodium, with atomic weights ranging from 18 to 37, although all of the higher atomic weight isotopes decay very rapidly and can only exist for a fraction of a second. Sodium 22 is chemically akin to the only stable sodium isotope, sodium 23, that we all eat as common salt in the form of NaCl (sodium chloride). However, sodium isotopes all have nuclei containing eleven protons. Sodium 22 is a very special and unusual isotope, because it emits particles called positrons, and as a result the element changes to neon 22. Positrons are actually antielectrons, or in layman's language antimatter. When matter and antimatter meet, they annihilate each other and release very large amounts of energy in the process.

Now that we have got the school lesson out of the way, we can begin to discuss the history of science.

CHAPTER 2

In order to gain an appreciation of how science has progressed up until modern times, I am now including a discussion covering the most significant and ground-breaking achievements in this field. Due to the ever-increasing rate of growth in our knowledge as the years have progressed, I am splitting this discussion into three separate sections.

The current section will deal with pioneering developments prior to 1930. This is because when Adolf Hitler became Chancellor of Germany in 1933, he banned the teaching and research of all ideas developed by Albert Einstein, as he considered this to be Jewish physics. German scientists therefore had to think in totally new directions, and as a result a series of major breakthroughs in many fields of physics and science were made.

The next section then deals with developments in science from the 1930s until the 1970s. I chose the 1970s as this was the time when I studied physics at university. This chapter will include advancements up until the time at which I graduated. It will also include information regarding the quite amazing achievements of the German scientists prior to and during World War II, together with many of the subsequent developments made by both Allied and Soviet scientists after they had access to this technological treasure trove.

The final of these three sections in the development of science covers the 1970s up to the present day. Developments in the fields of science, physics, engineering and astronomy during this period have been quite breathtaking, and I hope that the achievements that we discuss will be as fascinating to the reader as they are to me.

When looking at the early era of scientific developments I will start with Leonardo Da Vinci. Prior to Da Vinci, most of the early work was philosophy which is outside the scope of this book. He was born in Vinci, Italy in 1452, and in my opinion was one of the most talented men who ever lived. He was an extremely accomplished painter, sculptor, mathematician, engineer, astronomer, architect, musician, writer, botanist, anatomist, geologist, cartographer, and the list goes on.

Everyone knows about the priceless works of art that he created, including the *Mona Lisa* and the *Last Supper*, but I will limit our discussion to his scientific achievements.

Da Vinci had no formal education in mathematics or Latin, and most of his peer group at the time tended to ignore him. He was more of an observational scientist, but had a huge talent for making accurate theoretical deductions from the information that he collected. His engineering achievements however were quite remarkable.

His journals included a large number of practical inventions, and most people now believe that if the materials and manufacturing capabilities that we have today had existed in the 15th century, many of his inventions could have been successfully turned into working machines.

It appears from the content of his journals that he was planning a series of papers to be published on a variety of subjects. While Leonardo's experimentation followed clear scientific methods, a recent and exhaustive analysis by Capra of Leonardo as a scientist argues that he was a fundamentally different kind of scientist from Galileo, Newton and many of the other scientists who followed him in that, as a Renaissance Man, his theorising and his hypothesising integrated the arts and particularly painting.

During his lifetime Leonardo was valued as an engineer. In a letter to Ludovico il Moro he claimed to be able to create all sorts of machines both for the protection of a city and for siege. When he fled to Venice in 1499, he found employment as an engineer, and devised a system of moveable barricades to protect the city from attack.

He also had a scheme for diverting the flow of the Arno River, a project on which Niccolò Machiavelli also worked. Leonardo's journals include a vast number of inventions, both practical and impractical. They include musical instruments, hydraulic pumps, reversible crank mechanisms, finned mortar shells and a steam cannon.

In 1502, Leonardo produced a drawing of a single span 720 foot (220 metre) bridge as part of a civil engineering project for Ottoman Sultan Bayezid II of Constantinople. The bridge was intended to span an inlet at the mouth of the Bosporus known as the Golden Horn. Bayezid did not pursue the project because he believed that such a construction was impossible. Leonardo's vision was resurrected in 2001 when a smaller bridge based on his design was successfully constructed in Norway.

For much of his life, Leonardo was fascinated by the phenomenon of flight, and he produced many studies of the flight of birds, including his 1505 *Codex on the Flight of Birds*, as well as plans for several flying machines as mentioned earlier. The British television station Channel Four commissioned a documentary that was titled *Leonardo's Dream Machines*, broadcast in 2003. Leonardo's designs for machines such as a parachute and a giant crossbow were interpreted, constructed and then tested. Some of those designs proved a success, whilst others fared less well when tested practically.

As our knowledge of science progressed, many pioneers in this area had a very hard time. The fate of people who upset the status quo can be precarious, but this has been happening for centuries.

Galileo is often credited with inventing the telescope. However, the first recorded reference to a telescope-type device was in a patent filed by a Dutch lens maker called Hans Lippershey in 1608. The patent was entitled "for seeing things far away as if they were nearby". Galileo made improvements to this original design, and in 1609 constructed the first modern optical telescope that we are all familiar with today.

This then ushered in an era with many very intelligent and competent people who spent many years studying the night sky. Subsequently a new breed of astronomers declared that the Earth was not at the centre of the universe, and in fact we were within a solar system with the sun at its centre. This immensely important discovery was proven after years of meticulous observation and mathematical analysis.

Unfortunately for many of them, they were burned alive at the stake, as their observations and conclusions contradicted the teachings of certain religious groups at the time.

The same fate befell the first explorers who announced that the Earth was not in fact flat, but spherical. It seems that some religious groups need to be dragged kicking and screaming into every successive century when scientific proof contradicts the beliefs that they preach. This has not only happened in the distant past, but still goes on today.

The man who first developed spectacles (eyeglasses) was also brutally murdered. His crime was trying to improve on God's perfect design, which was totally unacceptable to some religious leaders at the time. It is lucky that this type of ignorance is on the decline today, as otherwise all of our doctors and cancer surgeons would probably be burned at the stake as well.

I am not trying to put down religion at all. I personally am not a religious man, but I do know right from wrong, good from evil, and I respect people who hold religious values. I believe that I became confused about religion when I was about eight or nine years old. My mother was a Quaker, and my sister and I were required to attend Quaker meetings every Sunday. They are not like most other religious services. In the meeting room, chairs are positioned in concentric circles around a central table with flowers.

All of the children had to sit in the outer circles and were forbidden from speaking. Occasionally one or two of the senior adult members would stand up and say something, but otherwise we would all sit in silence for an hour. At the time, I could see no difference between a Quaker meeting and the punishment of a school detention, but I think that every religion has its own individual way of expressing their beliefs.

CHAPTER 3

Following the work of Leonardo Da Vinci, the next major pioneer of scientific discovery was Nicolaus Copernicus. He was a Polish scientist born in 1473. Copernicus was a Renaissance astronomer and mathematician, and was the first scientist who recognised that the sun was at the centre of our solar system, and the universe did not revolve around the Earth.

In 1551, he published a series of astronomical tables that astronomers and astrologists of the time adopted, and his ideas quickly superseded those that had previously been accepted.

His work on heliocentric theory was revolutionary at the time, and the main points of his discoveries are summarised below, although some of his theories were later found to be incorrect.

1. There is no one centre of all the celestial circles or spheres.
2. The centre of the Earth is not the centre of the universe, but only of the lunar sphere.
3. All the spheres revolve about the sun as their midpoint.
4. The ratio of the Earth's distance from the sun to the

height of the firmament (outermost celestial sphere containing the stars) is so much smaller than the ratio of the Earth's radius to its distance from the sun that the distance from the Earth to the sun is imperceptible in comparison with the height of the firmament.

5. Whatever motion appears in the firmament arises not from any motion of the firmament, but from the Earth's motion. The Earth, together with its circumjacent elements, performs a complete rotation on its fixed poles in a daily motion, while the firmament and the highest heaven abide unchanged.

6. What appear to us as motions of the sun arise not from its motion, but from the motion of the Earth and our sphere, with which we revolve about the sun like any other planet. The Earth has, then, more than one motion.

7. The apparent retrograde and direct motion of the planets arises not from their motion but from the Earth's. The motion of the Earth alone, therefore, suffices to explain so many apparent inequalities in the heavens.

Luckily for Copernicus, he died in 1543 before the news of his work reached the Catholic Inquisition. Others who later expanded on his discoveries were not so lucky. It would be about another seventy years before any further major advancement was made in this field.

Tycho Brahe was a Danish nobleman, although he was born in Sweden in 1546. He is recognised for his accurate and comprehensive astronomical and planetary observations. At about the same time, another great mathematician and astrologer named Giordano Bruno was born in Italy in 1548.

Brahe made important contributions by devising the most precise instruments available, before the invention of the telescope, for observing the heavens. Brahe made his observations from an island in the sound between Denmark and Sweden called Hveen. Brahe's instruments allowed him to determine more precisely than had previously been possible the detailed motions of the planets. In particular, Brahe compiled extensive data on the planet Mars, which would later prove crucial to Kepler in his formulation of the laws of planetary motion, because it would be sufficiently precise to demonstrate that the orbit of Mars was not a circle but an ellipse.

The most important scientific contributions of Brahe were as follows:

1. He made the most precise observations that had yet been made by devising the best instruments available before the invention of the telescope.
2. His observations of planetary motion, particularly that of Mars, provided the crucial data for later astronomers like Kepler to construct our present model of the Solar System.
3. He made observations of a supernova (a new star, as he then thought) in 1572. We now know that a supernova is an exploding star, not a new star. This was a "star" that appeared suddenly where none had been seen before, and was visible for about eighteen months before fading from view. Since this clearly represented a change in the sky, prevailing opinion held that the supernova was not really a star, but some local phenomenon in the

atmosphere. One must remember that the heavens were supposed to be unchanging in the Aristotelian view. Brahe's meticulous observations showed that the supernova did not change position with respect to the other stars (no parallax). Therefore, it was a real star, not a local object. This was early evidence against the immutable nature of the heavens, although Brahe did not interpret the absence of parallax for stars correctly, as we discuss below.

4. Brahe made careful observations of a comet in 1577. By measuring the parallax for the comet, he was able to show that the comet was further away than the moon. This contradicted the teachings of Aristotle, who had held that comets were atmospheric phenomena. "Gases burning in the atmosphere" was a common explanation among Aristotelians. As for the case of the supernova, comets represented an obvious change in a celestial sphere that was supposed to be unchanging. Furthermore, it was very difficult to ascribe uniform circular motion to a comet.

5. He made the best measurements that had yet been made in the search for stellar parallax. Upon finding no parallax for the stars, he correctly concluded that either
   a) the Earth was motionless at the centre of the universe, or
   b) the stars were so far away that their parallax was too small to measure.

Not for the only time in human thought, a great thinker formulated a pivotal question correctly, but then made the wrong choice of possible answers. Brahe did not believe that the stars could possibly be so far away, and so concluded that the Earth was the centre of the universe and that Copernicus was wrong.

6. Brahe proposed a model of the Solar System that was intermediate between the Ptolemaic and Copernican models (it had the Earth at the centre). It proved to be incorrect, but was the most widely accepted model of the Solar System for a time.

Brach also made many other contributions to astronomy, and during his flamboyant life he lost part of his nose in a duel. He finally died in 1601 after his bladder burst.

Tycho Bruno also affirmed that the universe was homogeneous, and that essentially the same physical laws would operate everywhere, although the use of that term is anachronistic. For Bruno, space and time were both infinite. There was no room in his stable and his permanent universe theory for the Christian notions such as Divine Creation and the Last Judgement.

In Bruno's model, the sun was simply one more star, and the stars all suns, each with their own planets. Bruno saw a solar system of a sun/star with planets as the fundamental unit of the universe. All these planets constituted an infinite number of inhabited worlds, a philosophical position known as cosmic pluralism.

According to Bruno, an infinite God necessarily created an infinite universe, formed of an infinite number of solar systems, separated by vast regions full of Aether. This was because he believed that empty space could not exist. Bruno had not yet arrived at the concept of a galaxy.

Bruno believed that comets were part of stars, and not, as other people maintained at the time, divine instruments or heavenly messengers. Each comet was a world, a permanent celestial body, formed of the four basic elements. Bruno's cosmology is marked by infinitude, homogeneity and isotropy, with planetary systems distributed evenly throughout. Bruno believed that matter followed an active animistic principle. This is the most dramatic respect in which Bruno's cosmology differs from a modern scientific understanding of the universe.

During the late 16th century, and throughout the 17th century, Bruno's ideas were held up for ridicule, debate, or inspiration. Bruno's true, if partial, vindication would have to wait for the implications and impact of Newtonian cosmology.

Bruno's overall contribution to the birth of modern science is still controversial. Some scholars follow Frances Yates, stressing the importance of Bruno's ideas about the universe being infinite and lacking geocentric structure as a crucial cross-point between the old and the new. Others see Bruno's idea of multiple worlds as a forerunner of Everett's many worlds interpretation of quantum mechanics. However, Bruno's ground-breaking ideas were not well received by the Catholic church.

He went first to Padua, where he taught briefly, and applied unsuccessfully for the chair of mathematics, which was assigned instead to Galileo one year later. Bruno then moved to Venice in March 1592. For about two months he worked as an in-house tutor to Mocenigo. When Bruno announced his plan to leave Venice, his host, who was unhappy with the teachings he had received, denounced him to the Venetian Inquisition. They promptly had Bruno arrested.

Among the numerous charges of blasphemy and heresy brought against him in Venice based on Mocenigo's denunciation was his belief in the plurality of worlds, as well as accusations of personal misconduct. Bruno defended himself skilfully, stressing the philosophical character of some of his positions, denying others and admitting that he had had doubts on some matters of dogma. The Inquisition however asked for his transferral to Rome. After several months and some quibbling the Venetian authorities reluctantly consented and Bruno was sent to Rome in 1593.

In Rome, Bruno's trial lasted seven years during which time he was imprisoned, lastly in the Tower of Nona. Some important documents about the trial are lost, but others have been preserved, among them a summary of the proceedings that was rediscovered in 1940. The numerous charges against Bruno, based on some of his books as well as on witness accounts, included blasphemy, immoral conduct and heresy in matters of dogmatic theology, and involved some of the basic doctrines of his philosophy and cosmology. Luigi Firpo lists these charges made against Bruno by the Inquisition.

Bruno continued his defensive strategy, which consisted of bowing to the church's dogmatic teachings, while trying to preserve the basis of his philosophy. In particular Bruno held firm to his belief in the plurality of worlds, although he was admonished to abandon it. His trial was overseen by the Inquisitor Cardinal Bellarmine, who demanded a full recantation, which Bruno eventually refused. On 20th January 1600, Pope Clement VIII declared Bruno a heretic and the Inquisition issued a sentence of death.

He was turned over to the secular authorities and, on 17th February 1600 in the Campo de' Fiori, a central Roman market square, he was burned alive at the stake. His ashes were dumped into the River Tiber.

CHAPTER 4

Following the work of Brahe and Bruno, the next major steps in the field of scientific discovery were made by Galileo Galilei. Galileo was a physicist, mathematician, engineer and astronomer, born in Pisa, Italy in 1564. He discovered the Jovian moons Europa, Callisto, Ganymede and Io. His contribution to modern science was so significant that NASA named a space mission after him. The Galileo spacecraft was launched in 1989. It consisted of an orbiter and entry probe, and travelled to Jupiter to investigate the planet and its moons.

Galileo's greatest achievements resulted from his improvements to the first telescope, and consequent astronomical observations and support for Copernicanism. Galileo has been called the father of modern observational astronomy, the father of modern physics, and the father of modern science. His contributions to observational astronomy include the telescopic confirmation of the phases of Venus, the discovery of the four largest satellites of Jupiter (named the Galilean moons in his honour), and the observation and analysis of sunspots. Galileo also worked in applied science and technology, inventing an improved military compass and other instruments.

Galileo's championing of heliocentrism was controversial within his lifetime, when most subscribed to either geocentrism or the Tychonic system. He met with opposition from other astronomers, who doubted heliocentrism due to the absence of an observed stellar parallax. The matter was investigated by the Roman Inquisition in 1615, which concluded that heliocentrism was false and contrary to scripture, placing works advocating the Copernican system on the index of banned books and forbidding Galileo from advocating heliocentrism.

Galileo later defended his views in a subsequent book which appeared to attack Pope Urban VIII, thus alienating not only the Pope but also the Jesuits, who had both supported Galileo up until this point. He was tried by the Holy Office, then found to be vehemently suspect of heresy. He was forced to recant, and spent the rest of his life under house arrest. It was while Galileo was under house arrest that he wrote one of his finest works, *Two New Sciences*, in which he summarised the work he had done some forty years earlier on the two sciences now called kinematics and strength of materials.

Galileo's father, Vincenzo Galilei, a lutenist and music theorist, had performed experiments establishing perhaps the oldest known non-linear relation in physics: for a stretched string, the pitch varies as the square root of the tension. These observations lay within the framework of the Pythagorean tradition of music, well known to instrument makers, which included the fact that subdividing a string by a whole number produces a harmonious scale. Thus, a limited amount of mathematics had long related music and physical science, and young Galileo could see his own father's observations expand on that tradition.

Galileo was one of the first modern thinkers to clearly state that the laws of nature are mathematical. In *The Assayer* he wrote that philosophy is written in the language of mathematics, and its characters are triangles, circles and other geometric figures.

His mathematical analyses are a further development of a tradition employed by late scholastic natural philosophers, which Galileo learned when he studied philosophy. He displayed a peculiar ability to ignore established authorities, most notably Aristotelianism. In broader terms, his work marked another step towards the eventual separation of science from both philosophy and religion, which was a major development in human thought.

He was often willing to change his views in accordance with observation. In order to perform his experiments, Galileo had to set up standards of length and time, so that measurements made on different days and in different laboratories could be compared in a reproducible fashion. This provided a reliable foundation on which to confirm mathematical laws using inductive reasoning.

Galileo showed a remarkably modern appreciation for the proper relationship between mathematics, theoretical physics and experimental physics. He understood the parabola, both in terms of conic sections and in terms of the ordinate (y) varying as the square of the abscissa (x).

Galilei further asserted that the parabola was the theoretically ideal trajectory of a uniformly accelerated projectile in the absence of friction and other disturbances. He conceded that there are limits to the validity of this theory, noting on theoretical grounds that a projectile trajectory of a size comparable to that of the Earth could not possibly be a parabola, but he nevertheless maintained that for distances up to the range of the artillery of his day, the deviation of a projectile's trajectory from a parabola would be only very slight.

Soon after Galileo was born, his great contemporary Johannes Kepler came onto the scene. He was born in Weil der Stadt, Germany in 1571. In common with Galileo, Kepler's contribution to modern science is also considered to be so significant that NASA named one of its most famous space telescopes after him. The Kepler spacecraft was launched in 2009.

In October 1604, a bright new evening star appeared, but Kepler did not believe the rumours until he saw it himself. Kepler was a key figure in the 17th century scientific revolution. He is best known for his laws of planetary motion, which also provided one of the foundations for Isaac Newton's theory of universal gravitation.

During his career, Kepler was a mathematics teacher at a seminary school in Graz, Austria, where he became an associate of Prince Hans Ulrich von Eggenberg. Later he became an assistant to astronomer Tycho Brahe, and eventually the imperial mathematician to Emperor Rudolf II and his two successors.

He was also a mathematics teacher in Linz, Austria, and an advisor to General Wallenstein. Additionally, he did fundamental work in the field of optics, invented an improved version of the refracting telescope (the Keplerian Telescope), and made further telescopic developments following on from the work of his contemporary Galileo Galilei.

Kepler lived in an era when there was no clear distinction between astronomy and astrology, but there was a strong division between astronomy (a branch of mathematics within the liberal arts) and physics (a branch of natural philosophy).

Kepler described his new astronomy as celestial physics, and treated astronomy as part of a universal mathematical physics.

Kepler's first major astronomical work was the first published in defence of the Copernican system. Kepler claimed to have had an epiphany in 1595, while teaching in Graz, demonstrating the periodic conjunction of Saturn and Jupiter in the zodiac. He realised that regular polygons bound one inscribed and one circumscribed circle at definite ratios, which he reasoned, might be the geometrical basis of the universe.

After failing to find a unique arrangement of polygons that fit known astronomical observations (even with extra planets added to the system), Kepler began experimenting with three-dimensional polyhedra. He found that each of the five Platonic solids could be uniquely inscribed and circumscribed by spherical orbs. Nesting these solids, each encased in a sphere, within one another would produce six layers, corresponding to the six known planets – Mercury, Venus, Earth, Mars, Jupiter and Saturn.

By ordering the solids correctly as the basic geometrical solids known as octahedron, icosahedron, dodecahedron, tetrahedron and cube, he found that the spheres could be placed at intervals corresponding (within the accuracy limits of available astronomical observations) to the relative sizes of each planet's path. Kepler also found a formula relating the size of each planet's orb to the length of its orbital period: from inner to outer planets, the ratio of increase in orbital period is twice the difference in orb radius. However, Kepler later rejected this formula, because it was not precise enough.

In terms of the impact of his published work, it can be seen as an important first step in modernising the theory proposed by Nicolaus Copernicus in his *De Revolutionibus*. Whilst Copernicus sought to advance a heliocentric system in this book, he resorted to epicycles and eccentric circles in order to explain the change in a planets' orbital speed, and also continued to use as a point of reference the centre of the Earth's orbit rather than that of the sun.

Modern astronomy owes much to Kepler, despite some flaws in his deductions, since his work represents the first step in cleansing the Copernican system of the remnants of the Ptolemaic theory still clinging to it.

As the reader may be falling asleep by now from an overdose of science history, we will now take a look at Charles Darwin. Although he had absolutely nothing to do with physics, chemistry or gravity, he was a great man. He developed the theory of evolution, and his pioneering work is honoured by his marble statue that looks down over the main hall of the Natural History Museum in London.

For me, his greatest legacy is the annual award that bears his name. These awards are bestowed posthumously upon people who have excelled in improving the human gene pool.

I remember a few years ago this award was jointly bestowed on a brother and sister from Canada. They were impoverished students alone in their parents' house over the weekend. They had told their friends that they could not go out one evening, as they had no money at all. The rest of the story was pieced together from the forensic examination of the scene, and was reported in the local press.

This hapless pair apparently ran out of alcohol that evening, and post mortems showed petrol and milk in their stomachs. It was concluded that they mixed petrol from the lawnmower with milk, and then sat down by the lounge fire to watch TV and enjoy their drinks. Soon thereafter, one or both of them threw up in the fireplace, and the resulting explosion and fire destroyed the house.

I have recently nominated a scrap-yard worker from Thailand for the Darwin Award this year following a story reported by BBC World News. A construction worker excavating the foundations for a building in Bangkok unearthed an unexploded 500-pound World War II bomb. Instead of calling the bomb squad, he sold it to a local scrapyard. Due to its size, they decided to cut it up with an oxyacetylene torch.

When the emergency services arrived on the scene, they found that the building had been completely demolished. There was a 3-metre crater in the ground and body parts were discovered over 100 metres away from the centre of the detonation. I doubt that anyone else this year will be more deserving of this award. The reader can obtain details of all previous Darwin Awards on the web.

CHAPTER 5

Follow the work of Galileo and Kepler, very major steps forward in physics and mathematics were made by Isaac Newton, who would soon be knighted in recognition of his work. Newton was born in Woolsthorpe-by-Colsterworth in the UK in 1643. He is considered by many to be the father of modern physics and kinematics.

His work laid the foundations for further developments in these areas for all future physicists. Today, the basic unit of force is named after him. One Newton is defined as the force required to accelerate a mass of one kilogram at a rate of one metre per second squared.

His book *Mathematical Principles of Natural Philosophy*, first published in 1687, laid the foundations for classical mechanics. Newton also made major contributions in the fields of optics and calculus.

This book formulated the laws of motion and universal gravitation, which dominated scientists' view of the physical universe for the next three centuries. By deriving Kepler's laws of planetary motion from his mathematical description of gravity, and then using the same principles to account for the trajectories of comets, the tides, the precession of the equinoxes and other phenomena, Newton removed the last doubts about the validity of the heliocentric model of the cosmos.

This work also demonstrated that the motion of objects on Earth and of celestial bodies could be described by the same principles. His prediction that the Earth should be shaped as an oblate spheroid was later vindicated by the measurements of Maupertuis La Condamine and others, which helped convince most Continental European scientists of the superiority of Newtonian mechanics over the earlier system of Descartes.

Newton was a fellow of Trinity College and the second Lucasian Professor of Mathematics at the University of Cambridge. Later in his life, Newton became president of the Royal Society. He also served the British government as Warden and Master of the Royal Mint.

Newton's work is still taught to science students today, and his three laws of motion define kinematics. These laws state:

I. Every object in a state of uniform motion tends to remain in that state of motion unless an external force is applied to it.

II. The relationship between an object's mass (m), its acceleration (a) and the applied force (F) is $F=ma$.

Acceleration and force are vectors. In this law the direction of the force vector is the same as the direction of the acceleration vector.

III. For every action there is an equal and opposite reaction.

Newton also built the first practical reflecting telescope, and developed a theory of colour based on the observation that a prism decomposes white light into the many colours of the visible spectrum. He formulated an empirical law of cooling, studied the speed of sound and introduced the notion of a Newtonian fluid. In addition to his work on calculus, as a mathematician Newton contributed to the study of power series, generalised the binomial theorem to non-integer exponents and developed Newton's method for approximating the roots of a function.

In 1679, Newton returned to his work on celestial mechanics by considering gravitation and its effect on the orbits of planets with reference to Kepler's laws of planetary motion. This followed stimulation by a brief exchange of letters in 1679–80 with Hooke, who had been appointed to manage the Royal Society's correspondence, and who opened a correspondence intended to elicit contributions from Newton to Royal Society transactions.

Newton's reawakening interest in astronomical matters received further stimulus with the appearance of a comet in the winter of 1680–81, on which he corresponded with John Flamsteed. After the exchanges with Hooke, Newton worked out proof that the elliptical form of planetary orbits would result from a centripetal force inversely proportional to the square of the radius vector. Newton communicated his results to Edmond Halley and to the Royal Society in a tract written on about nine sheets, which was copied into the Royal Society's Register Book in December 1684.

Newton's book *The Principia* was published on 5th July 1687 with encouragement and financial help from Edmond Halley. In this work, Newton stated his three universal laws of motion that contributed to many advances during the Industrial Revolution which soon followed, and were not to be improved upon for more than 200 years. Many of these advancements continue to be the underpinnings of non-relativistic technologies in the modern world. He used the Latin word gravitas (weight) for the effect that would come to be known as gravity, and defined the law of universal gravitation.

In the same work, Newton presented a calculus-like method of geometrical analysis using first and last ratios, and gave the first analytical determination (based on Boyle's law) of the speed of sound in air. This inferred the oblateness of the spheroidal figure of the Earth, and accounted for the precession of the equinoxes as a result of the moon's gravitational attraction on the Earth's oblateness. This initiated the gravitational study of the irregularities in the motion of the moon, and provided a theory for the determination of the orbits of comets.

Newton made clear his heliocentric view of the Solar System. This was developed in a somewhat modern way, because already by the mid-1680s he recognised the deviation of the sun from the centre of gravity of the solar system. For Newton, it was not precisely the centre of the sun or any other body that could be considered at rest, but rather the common centre of gravity of the Earth, the sun and all of the planets. Newton observed that this centre of gravity either is at rest or moves uniformly forward.

Newton's postulation of an invisible force able to act over vast distances led to him being criticised for introducing occult agencies into science. Later, in the second edition of *The Principia* published in 1713, Newton firmly rejected such criticisms, concluding that it was enough that the phenomena implied a gravitational attraction, as they did. However they did not indicate its cause, and it was both unnecessary and improper to frame hypotheses of things that were not implied by the phenomena.

With *The Principia*, Newton became internationally recognised. He acquired a circle of admirers, including the Swiss-born mathematician Nicolas Fatio de Duillier, with whom he formed an intense relationship. This abruptly ended in 1693, and at the same time Newton suffered a nervous breakdown.

It would be another century before any further major steps forward were made in physics following the ground-breaking work of Sir Isaac Newton.

In 1777 another pioneering physicist named Hans Ørsted from Rudkøbing in Denmark appeared on the scene. He was the first physicist to discover that electrical currents create magnetic fields; the fundamental aspect of electromagnetism.

In 1819, he noticed the deflection of a compass needle while performing a demonstration for his students. The discovery of this basic cornerstone of physics, the demonstrable connection between electricity and magnetism, rocked the scientific community. It led to a flurry of activity in electro-dynamic research by such investigators as Ampère and Arago.

After all, the magnetism produced by a current would generate a force. Forces are capable of producing motion, so motion could come about which would lead to a current. While this is not a conservation law, it is a statement about the fundamental inter-convertibility of natural phenomena.

Ørsted's experiment showed that there were underlying connections between what appeared to be quite different physical phenomena, and encouraged other scientists to seek them out. In more recent times, connections between superconductors and gravity have been demonstrated, but our understanding of this phenomenon is still not complete. While universal convertibility is not the same as conservation, the two are nonetheless closely related. Thus, a connection or conversion between different phenomena, especially two as outwardly dissimilar as electricity and magnetism, was a step towards a unified concept of energy.

Today physicists are investigating what is known as "Zero Point Energy" and its connection to other established laws of physics. This energy form appears to defy some of our currently accepted laws of physics, but this has happened with many new discoveries over the centuries.

The Holy Grail in modern physics is to develop a unified field theory which ties up all of the loose ends and fills in all of the blanks in our current knowledge, but this may not be achieved for a very long time.

Until 1820, the only magnetism known was that of iron magnets and of "lodestones", natural magnets of iron-rich ore. It was believed that the inside of the Earth was magnetised in the same fashion, and scientists were greatly puzzled when they found that the direction of the compass needle at any place slowly shifted, decade by decade, suggesting a slow variation of the Earth's magnetic field.

On 21st April 1820, during a lecture, Ørsted noticed that a compass needle deflected from magnetic north when an electric current from a battery was switched on and off, confirming a direct relationship between electricity and magnetism. His initial interpretation was that magnetic effects radiate from all sides of a wire carrying an electric current, as do light and heat. Three months later he began more intensive investigations, and soon thereafter published his findings, showing that an electric current produces a circular magnetic field as it flows through a wire. This discovery was not due to mere chance, since Ørsted had been looking for a relation between electricity and magnetism for several years. The special symmetry of the phenomenon was possibly one of the difficulties that retarded the discovery.

It is sometimes claimed that the Italian scientist Gian Domenico Romagnosi was the first person who found a relationship between electricity and magnetism, about two decades before Ørsted's 1820 discovery of electromagnetism. Romagnosi's experiments showed that an electric current from a voltaic pile could deflect a magnetic needle. His researches were published in two Italian newspapers and were largely overlooked by the scientific community.

Ørsted's findings stirred much research into electrodynamics throughout the scientific community, influencing French physicist André-Marie Ampère's developments of a single mathematical formula to represent the magnetic forces between current-carrying conductors. Ørsted's work also represented a major step toward a unified concept of energy, and in 1822, he was elected as a foreign member of the Royal Swedish Academy of Sciences.

Soon after the advances made by Ørsted, his discoveries were further developed by Michael Faraday. He was an English scientist who contributed to the fields of electromagnetism and electrochemistry. His main discoveries include those of electromagnetic induction, diamagnetism and electrolysis. Faraday was born on 22nd September 1791, in Newington Butts in the UK.

Faraday received little formal education, but he was one of the most influential scientists in history. It was due to his research on the magnetic field around a conductor carrying a direct current that Faraday established the basis for the concept of the electromagnetic field in physics. He similarly discovered the principle of electromagnetic induction, diamagnetism and the laws of electrolysis. His inventions of electromagnetic rotary devices formed the foundation of electric motor technology, and it was largely due to his efforts that electricity became practical for use in technology.

As a chemist, Faraday discovered benzene, investigated the clathrate hydrate of chlorine, invented an early form of the Bunsen burner and the system of oxidation numbers, and popularised terminology such as anode, cathode, electrode and ion. Faraday ultimately became the first and foremost Fullerian Professor of Chemistry at the Royal Institution of Great Britain, a lifetime position.

Faraday was an excellent experimentalist, but his mathematical abilities, however, did not extend as far as trigonometry or any but the simplest algebra. James Clerk Maxwell took the work of Faraday and others, and summarised it in a set of equations that is accepted as the basis of all modern theories of electromagnetic phenomena. James Maxwell's achievements will be discussed in the next section.

On Faraday's use of the lines of force, Maxwell wrote that they show Faraday to have been in reality a mathematician of a very high order. Today the fundamental unit of capacitance, the Farad, is named in his honour.

Faraday is best known for his work regarding electricity and magnetism. His first recorded experiment was the construction of a voltaic pile (an early battery) with seven penny coins, stacked together with seven disks of sheet zinc, and six pieces of paper moistened with salt water. With this pile he decomposed sulphate of magnesia.

Faraday went on to build two devices to produce what he called "electromagnetic rotation". One of these, now known as the homopolar motor, caused a continuous circular motion that was engendered by the circular magnetic force around a wire.

This wire extended into a pool of mercury into which he placed a magnet. The wire would then rotate around the magnet if supplied with current from a chemical battery. These experiments and inventions formed the foundation of modern electromagnetic technology.

From his initial discovery in 1821, Faraday continued his laboratory work, exploring the electromagnetic properties of materials. In 1824, Faraday briefly set up a circuit to study whether a magnetic field could regulate the flow of a current in an adjacent wire, but he found no such relationship.

Two years after the death of Faraday's fellow physicist Humphry Davy in 1831, Faraday began his great series of experiments in which he discovered electromagnetic induction. Faraday's breakthrough came when he wrapped two insulated coils of wire around an iron ring, and found that upon passing a current through one coil, a momentary current was induced in the other coil. This phenomenon is now known as mutual induction.

In subsequent experiments, he found that if he moved a magnet through a loop of wire, an electric current flowed in that wire. The current also flowed if the loop was moved over a stationary magnet. His demonstrations established that a changing magnetic field produces an electric field. This relation was modelled mathematically by James Clerk Maxwell as Faraday's law, which subsequently became one of the four Maxwell equations. Faraday would later use the principles he had discovered to construct the electric dynamo, the ancestor of modern power generators and the electric motor.

In 1845, Faraday discovered that many materials exhibit a weak repulsion from a magnetic field – a phenomenon he termed diamagnetism. In his work on static electricity, Faraday's ice pail experiment demonstrated that the charge resided only on the exterior of a charged conductor, and exterior charge had no influence on anything enclosed within a conductor. This is because the exterior charges redistribute such that the interior fields due to them cancel. This shielding effect is used in what is now known as a Faraday cage.

CHAPTER 6

In some previous sections I have been criticising Christianity, and in particular the Catholic church and the Quakers. In order to try to redress the balance of the situation, I will now recall some of my encounters with other religions. I think that the underlying problem today is that what one group considers normal is totally abnormal to another group, and this often causes misunderstandings and conflicts.

I need to stress that I personally am not a religious man, but I have worked on every continent bar Antarctica in the course of my career in the worldwide oil and gas industry. I believe that every country and every religion has a lot of very good and devout people, but also some people who are not so savoury.

My first encounter with people in a non-Christian country was in Jordan. Jordan is a fantastic country and is steeped in history with many outstanding historical sites dating back to the dawn of modern history. The capital Amman, along with Damascus in Syria, are said to be two of the oldest continuously inhabited cities in the world. My agent at the time took me to a restaurant in the old part of the city, where it is said that Jesus Christ ate over 2,000 years ago. Jordan is also a very moderate Muslim state, and westerners along with people from all creeds are well received. However my insight into how the mind-set of some of the local people works occurred at that time.

I was working as a contractor on a land-based drilling rig in the very south of Jordan. I was around twenty-five years old at the time, and the assistant driller there was a Jordanian of about the same age. We got on very well, and when we were off shift we would spend a lot of time in each other's trailers talking and getting to know each other. On one occasion when he came over to my trailer, I was enjoying a beer as I was off shift for twelve hours.

We got talking about life in general, and he then asked if he could take one of my beers as he had never tried alcohol before. Not wishing to be rude, I offered him a beer. He asked me if I had ever had a girlfriend. I considered that to be a strange question to ask a twenty-five-year-old European, but I just replied "Yes, I have." He then started complaining that I was so lucky, as in his country it was impossible to get a girlfriend before a man is married.

After drinking two more bottles, he promptly fell asleep in his chair. An hour or so later he woke up, sat bolt upright in the chair, and asked me if any of my girlfriends had been virgins. He had obviously been dreaming about our conversation. I replied that I did not think so, but this is the 20th century so who really cares.

He then started ranting on about how he would never take a wife who had been with another man. I told him that in my culture this is about as important as if a female has worn denims in the past or not. This was an eye-opener for me, because the poor man did not understand the reason why he could not get a girlfriend, and that all of the problems he was complaining about were entirely of his own making.

Having said that, I have a lot of respect for the way in which some people evaluate situations in many Muslim countries. Saudi Arabia is considered to have one of the strictest Muslim regimes in the world. While working in Jordan, I needed to regularly travel from the rig site back to Amman in order to attend meetings and perform other duties.

One morning I needed to leave the rig site, but there had been a flash flood in the desert the previous day. Even though I was driving a 4x4 with lockable diffs, it was not possible for me to drive in the required direction. I therefore needed to make a major detour to avoid the floods. After several hours, I came across a road and headed in a northerly direction. I was running low on diesel at the time, so stopped at the first fuel station that I encountered. After filling the tank and my spare jerry cans I tried to pay the bill. It was then I realised that I was now in Saudi Arabia, but they accepted my US dollars for the fuel.

Being in Saudi Arabia when you have entered unlawfully with no visa, and you are also in a pickup truck with empty crates of beer bottles in the back, is not a comfortable position to be in. I considered my options, and figured that the only thing I could do was to carry on and try to get back into Jordan the best way I could. Before too long, I came upon a border crossing.

At this stage it was too late to turn back, as there were many armed Saudi police and soldiers at the checkpoint. I explained the situation to them, and after detaining me for twenty minutes or so they said that it was an honest mistake and that I could cross back into Jordan. This was very generous of them, as I could have been in a lot of trouble for this.

Back to the science, and we will now look at the developments made by James Clerk Maxwell. Maxwell was an outstanding Scottish mathematical physicist. His most famous achievements were to formulate a set of equations that described electricity and magnetism, and his work on the kinetic theory of gases. He was born on 13th June 1831 in Edinburgh, Scotland, and Maxwell's achievements concerning electromagnetism have been called the second great unification in physics after the initial work of Sir Isaac Newton.

With the publication of his work on the theory of electromagnetic fields in 1865, Maxwell demonstrated that electric and magnetic fields both travel through space as waves moving at the speed of light. Maxwell proposed that light is in fact undulations in the same medium that is the cause of electric and magnetic phenomena. The unification of light and electrical phenomena led to the prediction of the existence of radio waves.

Maxwell helped develop the Maxwell-Boltzmann distribution, which is a statistical means of describing aspects of the kinetic theory of gases. He is also known for making the first durable colour photograph in 1861.His discoveries helped usher in the era of modern physics, laying the foundation for future work in such fields as relativity and quantum mechanics. Many physicists regard Maxwell as the 19th century scientist who had the greatest influence on 20th century physics.

Maxwell had studied electricity and magnetism as early as 1855 after he read *On Faraday's lines of force*. This paper presented a simplified model of Faraday's work, and detailed how the two phenomena were related. Maxwell then reduced all of the current knowledge into a linked set of differential equations with twenty equations and twenty variables. This work was later published as *On physical lines of force* in 1861.

Around 1862, Maxwell calculated that the speed of propagation of an electromagnetic field is approximately that of the speed of light. He considered this to be more than just a coincidence.

Working on the problem further, Maxwell showed that his equations predicted the existence of waves that travel through empty space at a speed that could be predicted from simple electrical experiments. Using the data available at the time, Maxwell calculated this velocity to be 310,740,000 metres per second.

In his 1864 paper *A dynamical theory of the electromagnetic field*, Maxwell wrote, "The agreement of the results seems to show that light and magnetism are affections of the same substance, and that light is an electromagnetic disturbance propagated through the field according to electromagnetic laws".

His famous equations first appeared in fully developed form in a textbook in 1873. Maxwell's theory consists of four differential equations, known now collectively as Maxwell's Laws. These laws have stood the test of time, and his quantitative connection between light and electromagnetism is considered one of the great accomplishments of 19th century.

Maxwell also introduced the concept of the electromagnetic field in comparison to the force lines that Faraday described. By understanding the propagation of electromagnetism as a field emitted by active particles, Maxwell could advance his work on light. At that time, Maxwell believed that the propagation of light required a medium for the waves, dubbed Aether. Over time, the existence of such a medium, permeating all space and yet apparently undetectable by mechanical means, proved impossible to reconcile with experiments performed. These difficulties inspired Einstein to formulate the theory of special relativity, and in the process Einstein dispensed with the requirement of a stationary Aether.

Twenty-five years after Maxwell's birth, the great physicist, engineer and inventor Nikola Tesla was born. Although Tesla was born in Smiljan, Croatia, he spent most of his life in the USA. He was a physicist, electrical engineer, mechanical engineer and futurist best known for his contributions to the design of the modern alternating current electricity supply system.

I personally consider Nikola Tesla to be one of the greatest scientists and engineers of the recent era. His understanding of concepts including AC electricity and the transmission of energy through both cables and the atmosphere were leagues ahead of any of his peer group.

A testimony to his genius is that when he died in Manhattan, USA in 1943, his residence and lab were immediately raided by the US secret service. Many of the documents that they removed in 1943 still remain classified today, and cannot be obtained even under the Freedom of Information Act. This information is known to exist following Tesla's public demonstrations of many of his inventions, but his research notes on how these inventions were developed will not be shared. As is the case with all sensitive officially unpublished information, any enquiry is met with the standard reply that "no records can be found".

During his early career, Tesla briefly worked with Thomas Edison before the two parted ways. Edison did not understand AC theory, phase angles, power factors and other basic knowledge required in order to design an AC power transmission system. In order to transmit large amounts of power over long distances the only efficient way is to use very high voltages. This is because the power you can transmit is the product of the voltage times the current, and the size and weight of the power cables required are dictated by the current that they need to carry.

Therefore if you can increase the transmission voltage by 1,000 times, the cross-section of the conductor required to transmit the power can be reduced by 1,000 times. This principle is in worldwide use today, where main electricity transmission lines operate at several hundred thousand volts.

These very high voltages must be reduced to manageable levels before they can be used by industrial and domestic consumers. The only way to do this efficiently is by the use of transformers, which we are all familiar with in electricity substations and on local distribution poles. In order to change the voltage of DC power, devices such as DC-AC invertors or rotary converters must be used, which are both expensive and not that efficient.

These devices convert the DC power into AC which is required for the voltage conversion process. It is therefore difficult to understand why Edison did not want to generate his electricity as AC power in the first place.

Tesla's interest in electrical invention was likely sparked by his mother, Đuka Mandić, who invented small household appliances in her spare time while her son was growing up. Tesla's father, Milutin Tesla, was a priest. After studying in the 1870s at the Realschule, Karlstadt, the Polytechnic Institute in Graz, Austria and the University of Prague, Tesla began preparing for a trip to America.

Tesla travelled to the United States in 1884, and soon began working with Edison. While Edison was a power figure who focused on marketing and financial success, Tesla was commercially out-of-tune and therefore somewhat vulnerable. Tesla was however an extremely pivotal engineer, who pioneered some of history's most important inventions. His 1891 invention, the "Tesla coil", is still used in radio technology today.

On the AC electrical system alone, Tesla held forty basic US patents, which he later sold to George Westinghouse, an American engineer and businessman who was determined to supply the nation with Tesla's AC system. He would succeed in doing just that, not long after purchasing Tesla's patents. Around this time, conflict arose between Tesla and Edison, as Edison was determined to sell his direct current system to the nation. According to the Tesla Memorial Society of New York, Tesla and Westinghouse ultimately won out because Tesla's system was a superior technology, offering greater progress to both America and the world than Edison's DC system. Outside of his AC system patents, Tesla sold several other patent rights to Westinghouse.

At the 1893 World Columbian Exposition held in Chicago, Tesla conducted demonstrations of his AC system, which soon became the standard power system of the 20th century and has remained the worldwide standard ever since. Two years later, in 1895, Tesla designed the first hydroelectric power plant at Niagara Falls, a feat that was highly publicised throughout the world.

Around 1900, nearly a decade later and after inventing the Tesla coil, Tesla began working on his boldest project yet. He planned to build a global communications system using large electrical towers, for sharing information and to provide free electricity transmission throughout the world. The system, however, never came to fruition. It failed due to financial constraints, and Tesla had no choice but to abandon the Long Island, New York laboratory that housed his work on the tower project, Wardenclyffe. In 1917, the Wardenclyffe site was sold, and Tesla's tower was destroyed.

In addition to his AC systems and other pioneering work, throughout his career Tesla discovered, designed and developed ideas for a number of other important inventions. Most of these were officially patented by other inventors, including the dynamo and the induction motor. He also made great advances in the development of radar technology, X-ray technology and the rotating magnetic fields used in most modern AC equipment.

In the same year that Nikola Tesla was born, another great physicist and engineer named Joseph John Thomson was born in Manchester, England. His fundamental discoveries regarding cathode rays were the precursor to all future electronic equipment development up until the discovery of semiconductors, and the era of the transistor and the silicon chip integrated circuit.

Thomson was awarded the 1906 Nobel Prize in Physics for the discovery of the electron, and for his work on the conduction of electricity in gases. He was knighted in 1908 and appointed to the Order of Merit in 1912. In 1918 he became Master of Trinity College, Cambridge (strange how they tend to get the great physicists from Manchester University) where he remained until his death. He died in 1940 and was buried in Westminster Abbey, close to Sir Isaac Newton.

In 1897 Thomson showed that cathode rays were composed of a previously unknown negatively charged particle, and thus he is credited with the discovery and identification of the electron, and in a broader sense with the discovery of the first subatomic particle. Thomson is also credited with finding the first evidence for isotopes of a stable (non-radioactive) element in 1913, as part of his exploration into the composition of canal rays (positive ions). He invented the mass spectrometer.

Several scientists, such as William Prout and Norman Lockyer, had previously suggested that atoms were built up from a more fundamental unit, but they envisioned this unit to be the size of the smallest atom, hydrogen. Thomson, in 1897, was the first to propose that the fundamental unit was over a thousand times smaller than an atom, suggesting the subatomic particle now known as the electron.

Thomson discovered this through his explorations on the properties of cathode rays. Thomson made his suggestion in 1897 following his discovery that Lenard rays could travel much further through air than expected for an atom-sized particle. He estimated the mass of cathode rays by measuring the heat generated when the rays hit a thermal junction, and comparing this with the magnetic deflection of the rays.

His experiments suggested not only that cathode rays were over 1,000 times lighter than the hydrogen atom, but also that their mass was the same in whichever type of atom they came from. He concluded that the rays were composed of very light, negatively charged particles which were a universal building block of atoms. He called the particles "corpuscles", but later scientists preferred the name electron.

A month after Thomson's announcement of the corpuscle he found that he could reliably deflect the rays by an electric field if he evacuated the discharge tube to a very low pressure. By comparing the deflection of a beam of cathode rays by electric and magnetic fields, he obtained more robust measurements of the mass-to-charge ratio that confirmed his previous estimates. This became the classic means of measuring the charge and mass of the electron.

Thomson believed that the corpuscles emerged from the atoms of the trace gas inside his cathode ray tubes. He thus concluded that atoms were divisible, and that the corpuscles were their building blocks. To explain the overall neutral charge of the atom, he proposed that the corpuscles were distributed in a uniform sea of positive charge.

This was referred to by some at the time as the "plum pudding" model, assuming that the electrons were embedded in the positive charge like plums in a pudding, although in Thomson's model they were not stationary, but orbiting rapidly.

Thomson constructed a glass tube with a near-perfect vacuum. At the start of the tube was the cathode from which the rays projected. The rays were sharpened to a beam by two metal slits. The first of these slits doubled as the anode, and the second was connected to the earth. The beam then passed between two parallel aluminium plates, which produced an electric field between them when they were connected to a battery.

The end of the tube was a large sphere where the beam would impact on the glass, creating a glowing patch. Thomson pasted a scale to the surface of this sphere to measure the deflection of the beam. Note that any electron beam would collide with some residual gas atoms within the tube, thereby ionising them and producing electrons and ions within the tube. In previous experiments this space charge electrically screened the externally applied electrical field. However, in Thomson's tube, the density of residual atoms was so low that the space charge from the electrons and ions was insufficient to electrically screen the externally applied electric field, which permitted Thomson to successfully observe electrical deflection.

When the upper plate was connected to the negative pole of the battery and the lower plate to the positive pole, the glowing patch moved downwards, and when the polarity was reversed, the patch moved upwards.

Thomson imagined the atom as being made up of these corpuscles orbiting in a sea of positive charge. This was his plum pudding model. This model was later proved incorrect when his student Ernest Rutherford showed that the positive charge is concentrated in the nucleus of the atom.

CHAPTER 7

While reviewing the previous sections of this book, I noticed that I had referred to James Clerk Maxwell as being born in Edinburgh, UK. I have now changed this to Edinburgh, Scotland. Although Edinburgh, UK is perfectly correct, many Scots are very sensitive about this kind of thing.

I remember when Andy Murray (originally from Glasgow) brilliantly won the 2013 tennis grand slam final at Wimbledon, there was uproar in Scotland when he was described in the press as the first "British" player to win Wimbledon since Fred Perry in 1936. (Fred Perry was English).

Unfortunately you can find examples of this mind-set everywhere. Even in my home city of Aberdeen, this was going on all the time. Although I spent twenty-five years of my life based in Scotland, in my opinion the English have never truly been accepted by the Scots. Your first clue is when you drive north from England on the M6. North of Carlisle, there is a large sign by the motorway saying *Welcome to Scotland*. The graffiti below this sign reads *sorry about the s**t you had to drive through to get here*. Nice.

I do have some limited sympathy for the attitude of the Scots towards the English. For example, the first fast breeder nuclear reactor to be built in the UK was constructed at Dounreay, which is on the very northern tip of the Scottish mainland. This was as far away from London as possible, which baffled the Scots as they were told that this new technology (built to produce plutonium) was one hundred percent safe. So the Scots obviously asked why the government in London did not decide to build this facility in Birmingham or Manchester.

Another bone of contention came when Margaret Thatcher introduced the community charge, commonly called the poll tax. She imposed her new tax on the Scots first because almost nobody in Scotland voted for her party anyway. After one year of completely ignoring the complaints from the Scots, she imposed the same tax on the English. There was such an outcry that Thatcher had to remove the poll tax legislation completely from the statute books to avoid being thrown out of power.

Although I do have considerable sympathy for some of the treatment that the Scots have received at the hands of the English, I do think that they tend to go over the top on many occasions.

I remember the times in my local pub when England was playing in the final stages of the football World Cup, and Scotland had not qualified. All of the flags of the competing nations in the final rounds were suspended from the ceiling of the bar.

Every time that England was playing, the Scots would hang a large flag of the opposing team beneath the big screen TV. One year when England was finally knocked out by Portugal, the Portuguese flag remained hanging under the TV for a month.

I have never really understood why they behave in this way. When watching international sports tournaments such as the rugby Six Nations, I will obviously support England as I was born in England. However, if any of the other home nations of Scotland, Wales and Ireland are competing against teams from say France or Italy, I will support the home nations. I think that this underlines the basic difference between the thinking of the Scots from the rest of the UK population.

I have many friends in Scotland, and I am normally affectionately referred to as English Mike. However when they are inebriated and hunting in a pack, all of the English, including myself, are normally referred to as FEBs (figure it out for yourself). However you learn to live with this, and just let it roll off your back. The Scots are quite polite towards people from nations other than England.

My wife was from Norway. She, along with other Scandinavian females, were usually just referred to as blue-eyed barracudas, and the males as wooden tops. When it comes to racism, I think that many western governments feel intimidated by non-whites. In the UK everyone calls the British Brits, the Australians Aussies, but if you call Pakistanis Pakis that is racist. Who thought that one up?

The Scots sometimes go too far though, and they cannot get away with this type of behaviour when they verbally attack the non-European visitors. On one occasion there was a man from Nigeria who was staying in the hotel accommodation above our local bar. One evening he came down to the bar, and insisted that we changed the TV channel even though many locals were in the middle of watching a live sports programme.

After a heated discussion one of my friends, an elderly Scottish gentleman in his seventies, made a very derogatory racial comment to him, calling him an FBB. The Nigerian gentleman immediately called the police, who dropped what they were doing and had a squad car there within minutes.

My friend Dougie was promptly arrested, and after removing his belt and shoelaces they held him in a cell at the police HQ overnight. Dougie had his Black Labrador named Beth with him at the time, and I said to him that he should have told the police that he was talking to his dog.

The Nigerian gentleman in question worked for Shell and was on assignment for several months in Aberdeen. As there were several Shell employees in the bar at the time, this incident got back to the HR department at Shell the following morning. The Nigerian was on a plane back home the next day.

Now back to the science again. Following the discovery of the electron by J.J. Thomson, the next major step forward in our understanding of physics was made by Max Planck. Planck was a theoretical physicist who developed the theory of quantum mechanics, a cornerstone of modern physics. His work in this field won him the Nobel Prize for Physics in 1918.

He was born in 1858 in Kiel, Germany. His role as the originator of quantum theory revolutionised human understanding of atomic and subatomic processes, just as Albert Einstein's theory of relativity revolutionised the understanding of space and time. Together they constitute the fundamental theories of 20th century physics.

In 1894 Planck investigated the problem of black-body radiation. He had been commissioned by electric companies to create light bulbs emitting maximum light with minimum energy consumption. The problem had been looked at by Kirchhoff in 1859. He investigated how the intensity of the electromagnetic radiation emitted by a black body (a perfect absorber, also known as a cavity radiator) depended on the wavelength of the radiation (i.e. the colour of the light) and the temperature of the body. The question had been explored experimentally, but no theoretical treatment agreed with experimental values.

Planck's first proposed solution to the problem in 1899 followed on from what Planck called the "principle of elementary disorder". This allowed him to derive Wien's law from a number of assumptions about the entropy of an ideal oscillator, creating what was referred to as the Wien-Planck law. Soon it was found that the experimental evidence did not confirm the new law at all. Planck revised his approach, deriving the first version of his famous 1901 Planck black-body radiation law, which described the experimentally observed black-body spectrum well.

This first derivation did not include energy quantisation. Planck then revised this first approach, relying on a statistical interpretation of the second law of thermodynamics as a way of gaining a more fundamental understanding of the principles behind his radiation law.

The central assumption behind his new derivation was the supposition that electromagnetic energy could be emitted only in a quantised form. In other words, the energy could only be a multiple of an elementary unit. This is described by the equation $E = h / nu$ where h is Planck's constant, also known as Planck's action quantum (introduced already in 1899), and nu (the Greek letter nu, not the Roman letter v) is the frequency of the radiation.

Note that the elementary units of energy discussed here are represented by h / nu and not simply by h. Physicists now call these quanta photons, and a photon of frequency nu will have its own specific and unique energy. The total energy at that frequency is then equal to h / nu multiplied by the number of photons at that frequency. For any readers who are students starting to study quantum theory, this is an absolute basic to understand. Today this assumption, although incompatible with classical physics, is regarded as the birth of quantum physics and the greatest intellectual accomplishment of Planck's career.

The discovery of Planck's constant enabled him to define a new universal set of physical units (such as the Planck length and the Planck mass), all based on the fundamental physical constants upon which much of quantum theory is based. In recognition of Planck's fundamental contribution to a new branch of physics, he was awarded the Nobel Prize in Physics in 1918.

Subsequently, Planck tried to grasp the meaning of energy quanta, but to no avail. Even several years later, other physicists like Rayleigh, Jeans and Lorentz set Planck's constant to zero in order to align it with classical physics, but Planck knew full well that this constant had a precise nonzero value.

At the end of the 1920s, Bohr, Heisenberg and Pauli had worked out what was called the Copenhagen interpretation of quantum mechanics, but it was rejected by Planck, and by Schrödinger, Laue and Einstein as well. Planck expected that wave mechanics would soon render quantum theory (his own child) unnecessary. This was not to be the case, however. Further work only cemented the concept of quantum theory.

When the Nazis seized power in 1933, Planck was seventy-four. He witnessed many Jewish friends and colleagues expelled from their positions and humiliated, and hundreds of scientists wanted to emigrate from

Germany. Planck tried to persuade them to stay and continue working. He hoped the crisis would abate soon and the political situation would improve.

The next great physicist and chemist of this era was Ernest Rutherford. He was a New Zealand-born Canadian/British physicist who became known as the father of nuclear physics. He was born in 1871 in Brightwater, New Zealand, and died in 1937 in Cambridge, UK. He was knighted in 1914, and is also a Nobel Laureate.

Early in his career he discovered the concept of radioactive half-life, and proved that radioactivity involved the transmutation of one chemical element into another. He also differentiated and named alpha and beta radiation. This work was done at McGill University in Canada. It was the basis for the Nobel Prize in Chemistry he was awarded in 1908.

Rutherford moved in 1907 to the University of Manchester (a great seat of physics) in the UK, where he and Thomas Royds proved that alpha radiation is created by helium ions. Rutherford performed his most famous work after he became a Nobel Laureate. In 1911, although he could not prove whether it was positive or negative, he theorised that atoms have their charge concentrated in a very small nucleus, and thereby pioneered the Rutherford model of the atom.

This was brought about through his discovery and interpretation of Rutherford scattering in his gold foil experiment. He is also credited as the first scientist to split the atom. He achieved this breakthrough at Manchester University in 1917 in a nuclear reaction between nitrogen and alpha particles, in which he also discovered and named the proton. He was then promptly poached by Cambridge University.

Rutherford became Director of the Cavendish Laboratory at Cambridge University in 1919. Under his leadership the neutron was discovered by James Chadwick in 1932. In the same year, the first experiment to split the atomic nucleus in a fully controlled manner was performed by his students John Cockcroft and Ernest Walton working under his supervision. After his death in 1937, he was honoured by being interred with the greatest scientists of the United Kingdom, near Sir Isaac Newton's tomb in Westminster Abbey. The chemical element Rutherfordium was named after him in 1997.

At Cambridge, Rutherford started to work with J.J. Thomson on the conductive effects of X-rays on gases. This made advancements based on the work which led to the discovery of the electron by Thomson in 1897. Hearing of Becquerel's experience with uranium, Rutherford started to explore its radioactivity, discovering two types that differed from X-rays in their penetrating power. Continuing his research in Canada, he coined the terms alpha ray and beta ray in 1899 to describe the two distinct types of radiation.

He then discovered that thorium gave off a gas, which produced an emanation which was itself radioactive and would coat other substances. He found that a sample of this radioactive material of any size invariably took the same amount of time for half of the sample to decay, known as its "half-life" (eleven-and-a-half minutes in this case).

From 1900 to 1903, he was joined at McGill by the young chemist Frederick Soddy (Nobel Prize in Chemistry, 1921), for whom he set the problem of identifying the thorium emanations. Once he had eliminated all the normal chemical reactions, Soddy suggested that it must be one of the inert gases, which they named thoron (later found to be an isotope of radon). They also found another type of thorium that they called Thorium X, and kept on finding traces of helium. They also worked with samples of "Uranium X" from William Crookes, and radium from Marie Curie.

In 1902, they produced a "Theory of Atomic Disintegration" to account for all their experiments. Up until then atoms were assumed to be the indestructible basis of all matter, and although Curie had suggested that radioactivity was an atomic phenomenon, the idea of the atoms of radioactive substances breaking up was a radically new idea. Rutherford and Soddy demonstrated that radioactivity involved the spontaneous disintegration of atoms into other types of atoms (one element spontaneously being changed into another).

In 1903, Rutherford considered a type of radiation discovered, but not yet named, by French chemist Paul Villard in 1900, as an emission from radium. He realised that this observation must represent something different from his own alpha and beta rays, due to its very much greater penetrating power. Rutherford therefore gave this third type of radiation the name of gamma rays. All three of Rutherford's terms are in standard use today. Other types of radioactive decay have since been discovered, but Rutherford's three types are the most common.

In Manchester, he continued to work with alpha radiation. In conjunction with Hans Geiger, he developed zinc sulphide scintillation screens and ionisation chambers to count alphas. By dividing the total charge they produced by the number counted, Rutherford decided that the charge on the alpha was two. In late 1907, Ernest Rutherford and Thomas Royds allowed alphas to penetrate a very thin window into an evacuated tube. As they sparked the tube into discharge, the spectrum obtained from it changed as the alphas accumulated in the tube. Eventually, the clear spectrum of helium gas appeared, proving that alphas were at least ionised helium atoms, and probably helium nuclei.

Before leaving Manchester in 1919 to take over the Cavendish laboratory in Cambridge, Rutherford became the first person to deliberately transmute one element into another. In this experiment, he had discovered peculiar radiations when alphas were projected into air, and narrowed the effect down to the nitrogen, not the oxygen in the air. Using pure nitrogen, Rutherford used alpha radiation to convert nitrogen into oxygen through the nuclear reaction $^{14}N + \alpha \rightarrow\ ^{17}O + proton$.

A construction of nuclei where a single element could have different atomic weights, and therefore contain other matter, had been inferred for many years. It was also found that the different atomic weights all varied as whole numbers (that of the weight of hydrogen). Hydrogen was known to be the lightest element, and its nuclei presumably the lightest nuclei. Because of all of this evidence, Rutherford decided that a hydrogen nucleus was possibly a fundamental building block of all nuclei, and also possibly a new fundamental particle as well. Thus Rutherford postulated the hydrogen nuclei to be a new particle in 1920, which he called the proton.

In 1921, while working with Niels Bohr, Rutherford theorised about the existence of neutrons, which could somehow compensate for the repelling effect of the positive charges of protons. This could occur by causing an attractive nuclear force, and thus keep the nuclei from flying apart from the repulsion between the protons. The only alternative to neutrons was the existence of "nuclear electrons" which would counteract some of the proton charges in the nucleus, since by then it was known that nuclei had about twice the mass that could be accounted for if they were simply assembled from hydrogen nuclei (protons). But how these nuclear electrons could be trapped in the nucleus was a mystery.

Rutherford's theory of neutrons was proved in 1932 by his associate James Chadwick, who recognised neutrons immediately when they were produced by other scientists and later by himself, in bombarding beryllium with alpha particles. In 1935, Chadwick was awarded the Nobel Prize in Physics for this discovery.

Rutherford's research, and the work done under him as laboratory director, established the nuclear structure of the atom and the essential nature of radioactive decay as a nuclear process. Rutherford's team, using natural alpha particles, demonstrated nuclear transmutation. He is known as the father of nuclear physics. Rutherford died too early to see Leó Szilárd's idea of controlled nuclear chain reactions come into being.

Eight years after the birth of Rutherford, another true icon of modern theoretical physics, Albert Einstein, was born in Ulm, Germany. Einstein developed the general theory of relativity, one of the two pillars of modern physics. He is best known for his mass-energy equivalence formula $E = mc^2$. He is also a Nobel Physics Laureate.

Albert Einstein started his career as a patent clerk. While working, Einstein evaluated patent applications for electromagnetic devices. He quickly mastered the job, leaving him time to ponder on the transmission of electrical signals and electrical-mechanical synchronisation, an interest he had been cultivating for several years. While at the polytechnic school he had studied Scottish physicist James Maxwell's electromagnetic theories which describe the nature of light, and discovered a fact unknown to Maxwell himself: that the speed of light remained constant. However, this violated Isaac Newton's laws of motion because there is no absolute velocity in Newton's theory.

This insight led Einstein to formulate the principle of relativity.

In 1905 (often called Einstein's "miracle year") he submitted a paper for his doctorate and had four papers published in the *Annalen der Physik*, one of the best-known physics journals. The four papers (the photoelectric effect, Brownian motion, special relativity, and the equivalence of matter and energy) would alter the course of modern physics and bring him to the attention of the academic world. In his paper on matter and energy, Einstein deduced the well-known equation $E = mc^2$, suggesting that tiny particles of matter could be converted into huge amounts of energy, foreshadowing the development of nuclear power. There have been claims that Einstein and his wife, Mileva Marić, collaborated on his celebrated 1905 papers, but historians of physics who have studied the issue find no evidence that she made any substantive contributions. In fact, in the papers, Einstein only credits his conversations with Michele Besso in developing relativity.

At first Einstein's 1905 papers were ignored by the physics community. This began to change when he received the attention of Max Planck, perhaps the most influential physicist of his generation and founder of quantum theory. With Planck's complimentary comments and his experiments that confirmed his theories, Einstein was invited to lecture at international meetings, and he rose rapidly in the academic world. He was offered a series of positions at increasingly prestigious institutions, including the University of Zürich, the University of Prague, the Swiss Federal Institute of Technology and finally the University of Berlin, where he served as director of the Kaiser Wilhelm Institute for Physics from 1913 to 1933. As his fame spread, Einstein's marriage fell apart.

But hey, it can happen to anyone. My own marriage started getting ropey when my wife started accusing me of being sexist. I was very upset by this, but what can you do? It happened when we were watching a TV comedy show featuring Billy Connolly and his wife Pamela Stephenson. They are both world-class comedians and entertainers. After a heated discussion on the difference between the sexes, Billy Connolly asked her why, if women are so good at multitasking, are they unable to have a headache and sex at the same time. I thought that this was hilarious, but my wife considered it to be sexist. Things went downhill from there. I guess that everybody gets fed up with me eventually, as some years later she filed for divorce.

Under the Family Scotland Act (1996), it is irrelevant how poorly either the husband or the wife have behaved. It is sufficient just to say that the marriage had run its course (whatever that means) and a divorce is granted with the couple's assets being split 50-50.

I remember that at the final divorce hearing my poor sense of humour finally got the better of me. The Sheriff presiding over this hearing was a frosty octogenarian lady, who clearly had no sense of humour at all. After I had been dragged across the coals for over two hours, she asked me if everything had been declared fairly and honestly, to confirm that she was now in a position to make a judgement based on the required 50-50 split.

I had lost the plot by this time, and informed her that she had not taken into account my wife's breasts. As I had paid for the implants, I suggested that the law required me to take possession of one of her breasts. The sheriff then informed me that if I made any other similar comments, I would be held in contempt of court. I then said that if I could not get custody of one of her breasts, could I have access to one at the weekends. I was held in contempt and taken down to the cells.

OK, back to the science.

Due to Einstein's constant travel and the intense study required by his work, the arguments about his children and the family's meagre finances led Einstein to the conclusion that his marriage was over. Einstein began an affair with a cousin, Elsa Löwenthal, whom he later married. He finally divorced his wife Mileva in 1919 and as a settlement agreed to give her the money he might receive if he ever won a Nobel Prize.

In November 1915, Einstein completed the general theory of relativity, which he considered his masterpiece. He was convinced that general relativity was correct because of its mathematical beauty, and because it accurately predicted the perihelion of Mercury's orbit around the sun, which fell short in Newton's theory. General relativity theory also predicted a measurable deflection of light around the sun when a planet or another sun oribited near the sun. That prediction was confirmed in observations by British astronomer Sir Arthur Eddington during the solar eclipse of 1919. In 1921, Albert Einstein received word that he had received the Nobel Prize for Physics. Because relativity was still considered controversial, Einstein received the award for his explanation of the photoelectric effect.

In the 1920s, Einstein launched the new science of cosmology. His equations predicted that the universe is dynamic, ever expanding or contracting. This contradicted the prevailing view that the universe was static, a view that Einstein had held earlier, and which was a guiding factor in his development of the general theory of relativity. But his later calculations in the general theory indicated that the universe could be expanding or contracting. In 1929, astronomer Edwin Hubble found that the universe was indeed expanding, thereby confirming Einstein's work. In 1930, during a visit to the Mount Wilson Observatory near Los Angeles, Einstein met with Hubble and declared the cosmological constant, his original theory of the static size and shape of the universe, to be his "greatest blunder".

While Einstein was touring much of the world speaking on his theories in the 1920s, the Nazis were rising to power under the leadership of Adolf Hitler. Einstein's theories on relativity became a convenient target for Nazi propaganda. In 1931, the Nazis enlisted other physicists to denounce Einstein and his theories as Jewish physics. At this time, Einstein learned that the new German government, now fully controlled by the Nazi party, had passed a law barring Jews from holding any official position, including teaching at universities. Einstein also learned that his name was on a list of assassination targets, and a Nazi organisation published a magazine with Einstein's picture and the caption *Not Yet Hanged* on the cover.

In December 1932, Einstein decided to leave Germany forever. He took a position at the newly formed Institute for Advanced Study at Princeton, New Jersey, which soon became a Mecca for physicists from around the world. It was here that he would spend the rest of his career trying to develop a unified field theory, an all-embracing theory that would unify the forces of the universe, and thereby the laws of physics, into one framework. This would refute the accepted interpretation of quantum physics. Other European scientists also fled various countries threatened by Nazi takeover and came to the United States. Some of these scientists knew of Nazi plans to develop an atomic weapon. For a time, their warnings to Washington went unheeded.

In the summer of 1939, Einstein, along with another scientist, Leó Szilárd, was persuaded to write a letter to President Franklin D. Roosevelt to alert him of the possibility of a Nazi atomic bomb. President Roosevelt could not risk the possibility that Germany might develop an atomic bomb first. The letter is believed to be the key factor that motivated the United States to investigate the development of nuclear weapons. Roosevelt invited Einstein to meet with him and soon after the United States initiated the Manhattan Project.

Not long after he began his career at the Institute in New Jersey, Albert Einstein expressed an appreciation for the "meritocracy" of the United States and the right people had to think what they pleased, which was something he didn't enjoy as a young man in Europe. In 1935, Albert Einstein was granted permanent residency in the United States and became an American citizen in 1940. As the Manhattan Project moved from the drawing board to testing and development at Los Alamos, New Mexico, many of his colleagues were asked to develop the first atomic bomb, but Einstein was not one of them.

According to several researchers who examined FBI files over the years, the reason was that the US government didn't trust Einstein's lifelong association with peace and socialist organisations. FBI director J. Edgar Hoover went so far as to recommend that Einstein be kept out of America by the Alien Exclusion Act, but he was overruled by the US State Department. Instead, during the war, Einstein helped the US Navy evaluate designs for future weapons systems and contributed to the war effort by auctioning off priceless personal manuscripts. He sold a handwritten copy of his paper on special relativity for $6.5 million, and it is now in the Library of Congress.

On 6th August 1945, while on vacation, Einstein heard the news that an atomic bomb had been dropped on Hiroshima, Japan. He soon became involved in an international effort to try to bring the atomic bomb under control, and in 1946, he formed the Emergency Committee of Atomic Scientists with physicist Leó Szilárd. In 1947, in an article that he wrote for *The Atlantic Monthly*, Einstein argued that the United States should not try to monopolise the atomic bomb, but instead should supply the United Nations with nuclear weapons for the sole purpose of maintaining a deterrent. At this time, Einstein also became a member of the National Association for the Advancement of Coloured People. He corresponded with civil rights activist W. E. B. Du Bois and actively campaigned for the rights of African-Americans.

After the war, Einstein continued to work on many key aspects of the theory of general relativity, such as wormholes, the possibility of time travel, the existence of black holes and the creation of the universe. However, he became increasingly isolated from the rest of the physics community. The huge developments in unravelling the secrets of atoms and molecules were spurred on by the development of the atomic bomb. The majority of scientists were working using quantum theory, not relativity. Another reason for Einstein's detachment from his colleagues was his obsession with discovering his unified field theory. In the 1930s, Einstein engaged in a series of historic private debates with Niels Bohr, the originator of the Bohr atomic model. In a series of "thought experiments", Einstein tried to find logical inconsistencies in the quantum theory, but was unsuccessful. However, in his later years, he stopped opposing quantum theory and tried to incorporate it, along with light and gravity, into the larger unified field theory he was developing.

In the last decade of his life, Einstein withdrew from public life, rarely traveling far and confining himself to long walks around Princeton with close associates, whom he engaged in deep conversations about politics, religion, physics and his unified field theory.

On 17th April 1955, while working on a speech he was preparing to commemorate Israel's seventeenth anniversary, Einstein suffered an abdominal aortic aneurysm and experienced internal bleeding.

He was taken to the University Medical Centre at Princeton for treatment, but refused surgery, believing that he had lived his life and was content to accept his fate. "I want to go when I want," he stated at the time. "It is tasteless to prolong life artificially. I have done my share and it is time to go. I will do it elegantly." Einstein died at the University Medical Centre early the next morning on 18th April 1955 at the age of seventy-six.

During the autopsy, Thomas Stoltz Harvey removed Einstein's brain, seemingly without the permission of his family, for preservation and future study by doctors of neuroscience. His remains were cremated and his ashes were scattered in an undisclosed location. After decades of study, Einstein's brain is now located at the Princeton University Medical Centre.

We will conclude the discussion of other pioneering physicists Niels Bohr, Erwin Schrödinger, James Chadwick and Werner Heisenberg in the next section covering scientific advances made between 1930 and 1970. Although all of these scientists were born between 1885 and 1901, their main achievements were made in the 1930s.

CHAPTER 8

When looking at the explosion in scientific advances made between 1930 and 1970, one must appreciate that the astonishing German advances made up until mid-1945 were all under the control of the Nazis and the SS. The main figures in this area were changed frequently at Hitler's whim, and to fully understand what was happening we need to understand the hierarchy within the Schutzstaffel (SS). Long before Hitler became German chancellor in 1933, the SS was well established.

For one of the many examples of the confusion and disinformation created during this period, look no further than Wernher von Braun. When he was taken to the USA in 1945, the Americans also took Wehrmacht (Army) General Walter Dornberger, who they claimed was Wernher von Braun's boss. This was pure window dressing for American public consumption. US intelligence knew full well that Von Braun was a Major in the SS, and had used slave labour from concentration camps to build his V2 rockets. He would have seen these labourers beaten, hanged and worked to death on a daily basis. Von Braun actually reported directly to SS General Hans Kammler. Kammler held the third highest position in the SS, but the Americans knew that the truth would not go down well with the powerful Jewish lobby in Washington.

From 1929 onwards and throughout World War II, the top commander (Reichsführer) of the SS was Heinrich Himmler. At the outbreak of war, his number two was generally accepted to be Rudolf Hess, as although he was at the time Hitler's deputy, he also held the rank of General in the SS. However in 1941, Rudolf Hess flew alone to Scotland, was arrested and spent the rest of the war in the Tower of London.

Following this, the next man to be appointed to the position of SS second-in-command was Reinhard Heydrich. He was an SS Obergruppenführer, which was the equivalent rank to a five-star general in the Wehrmacht and most other armies. Heydrich was subsequently assassinated in Prague in May 1942 by Czech and Slovak commandos trained by British Intelligence. Although the assassination attempt was initially bungled, he died from his injuries a week later. The vacant SS number two position was then given to SS Obergruppenführer Oswald Pohl.

During the second half of World War II, the SS number three position was occupied by SS Obergruppenführer Hans Kammler. He had achieved a meteoric rise through the ranks of the SS due to his intelligence, ruthlessness, organisational skills and talent for understanding advanced technologies.

He was originally educated as a Dr of Engineering, but throughout the war he masterminded the SS takeover of virtually all of the important military manufacturing from Albert Speer and the armament ministry, and absolutely all of the high-technology research and development.

His achievements and the towering breakthroughs made by his group of scientists and engineers were truly ground-breaking, and the security system that he put in place to surround and protect these operations was never broken. Apart from Hitler himself, it is believed that no other member of the Nazi party knew of his work, let alone anyone on the Allied side. The work of his group is so significant that a section will be devoted to their achievements later in the book.

In the dying days of the war, another SS Obergruppenführer named Ernst Kaltenbrunner was promoted to the number two position in the SS. However, this was only after Kammler and Pohl had disappeared off the radar, leaving Himmler and Kaltenbrunner to their fate as the Third Reich collapsed. Some people have commented that the SS uniforms were very impressive. They should be, as they were designed and made by Hitler's good friend Hugo Boss.

We will now look at the main figures responsible for the scientific advances during the 1930s and 1940s. Niels Bohr was a Danish physicist who made great contributions to the understanding of atomic structure and quantum theory, for which he received the Nobel Prize for Physics in 1922. He was born in 1885 in Copenhagen, Denmark.

Bohr went on to become an accomplished physicist who came up with a revolutionary theory on atomic structures and radiation emission. After working on the Manhattan Project in the United States, Bohr, like Einstein, called for responsible and peaceful applications of atomic energy across the world.

Bohr's own research led him to theorise in a series of articles that atoms give off electromagnetic radiation as a result of electrons jumping to different orbit levels, departing from a previous model by Ernest Rutherford. Although Bohr's discovery would eventually be tweaked by other scientists, his ideas formed the basis of future atomic research.

After teaching at Manchester University, Bohr settled again at Copenhagen University in 1916 with a professorship position. Then, in 1920, he founded the university's Institute of Theoretical Physics, which he would run indefinitely.

Bohr worked with Werner Heisenberg and other scientists on a new quantum mechanics principle connected to Bohr's concept of complementarity, which was initially presented at an Italian conference in 1927. The concept asserted that physical properties on an atomic level would be viewed differently depending on experimental parameters, hence explaining why light could be seen as both a particle and a wave. Bohr would also come to apply this idea philosophically as well, with the belief that evolving concepts of physics deeply affected human perspectives. Another physicist by the name of Albert Einstein didn't fully see eye-to-eye with all of Bohr's assertions, and their talks became renowned in scientific communities.

Bohr went on to work with the group of scientists who were at the forefront of research on nuclear fission during the late 1930s, to which he contributed the liquid droplet theory. Outside of his pioneering ideas, Bohr was known for his wit and warmth, and his humanitarian ethics would greatly influence his later work.

With Adolf Hitler's rise in power, Bohr was able to offer German Jewish physicists refuge at his institute in Copenhagen, which in turn led to travel to the United States for many. Once Denmark became occupied by Nazi forces, the Bohr family escaped to Sweden, with Bohr and his wife eventually making their way to the US as well. Bohr then worked with the Manhattan Project in Nevada, where the first atom bomb was being created. Because he had concerns about how the bomb could be used, he called for future international arms control and active communication about the weapon between nations. This idea met with resistance from Winston Churchill and Franklin D. Roosevelt.

After the end of the war, Bohr returned to Europe and continued to call for peaceful applications of atomic energy. In his "Open Letter to the United Nations," dated 9th June 1950, Bohr envisioned an "open world" mode of existence between countries that abandoned isolationism for true cultural exchange.

In 1954, he helped to establish CERN, the European-based particle physics research facility, and put together the Atoms for Peace Conference of 1955. In 1957, Bohr received the Atoms for Peace Award for his trailblazing theories and efforts to use atomic energy responsibly.

Bohr was a prolific writer with more than a hundred publications to his name. After having a stroke, he died on 18th November 1962, in Copenhagen. Bohr's son, Aage, shared with two others the 1975 Nobel Prize in Physics for his research on motion in atomic nuclei.

Two years after Bohr came another great physicist, Erwin Schrödinger. I remember his work well, as all undergraduate physics students in my day had to be able to derive the famous "Schrödinger Equation" from first principles.

Born in 1887 in Vienna, Austria, Erwin Schrödinger went on to become a famed theoretical physicist and scholar who came up with a ground-breaking wave equation for electron movements. He was awarded the 1933 Nobel Prize in Physics, along with British physicist P.A.M. Dirac, and later became a director at Ireland's Institute for Advanced Studies.

Schrödinger joined the University of Zurich in 1921.His tenure as a professor at Zurich over the next six years would prove to be one of the most important periods of his physics career. Immersing himself in an array of theoretical physics research, Schrödinger came upon the work of fellow physicist Louis de Broglie in 1925, which sparked his interest in explaining that an electron in an atom would move as a wave, contrary to de Broglie's belief. The following year, he wrote a revolutionary paper that highlighted what would be known as the Schrödinger wave equation.

Following the atomic model of Niels Bohr and a thesis from de Broglie, Schrödinger articulated the movements of electrons in terms of wave mechanics as opposed to particle leaps. He provided a mode of thought to scientists that would become accepted and incorporated into thousands of papers, thus becoming an important cornerstone of quantum theory. Schrödinger made this discovery in the 1930s, with most theoretical physicists sharing ground-breaking finds during this period.

Schrödinger then left his position at Zurich for a new, prestigious opportunity at the University of Berlin, where he met Albert Einstein. He held this position until 1933, opting to leave upon the rise of Adolf Hitler's Nazi Party and the related persecution of Jewish citizens.

Shortly after joining the faculty of physics at Oxford University in England, Schrödinger learned that he had won the 1933 Nobel Prize in Physics, sharing the award with another quantum theorist, Paul A.M. Dirac. In his Nobel Prize acceptance speech, Schrödinger stated that his mentor, Fritz Hasenöhrl, would have been accepting the award if he had not died during World War I.

Following a three-year stay at Oxford, Schrödinger travelled and worked in different countries, including in Austria at the University of Graz. In 1939, he was invited by Irish Prime Minister Éamon de Valera to work at the Institute for Advanced Studies in Dublin, Ireland, heading its School for Theoretical Physics. He remained in Dublin until the mid-1950s, returning in 1956 to Vienna, where he continued his career at his alma mater.

Four years after the birth of Schrödinger, James Chadwick made further great advances in developing our knowledge of physics. Chadwick was an English physicist, who was awarded the 1935 Nobel Prize in physics for his discovery of the neutron in 1932. He was born in 1891, in Bollington, UK, and educated at Manchester University, where he studied under Rutherford. After the war, Chadwick followed Rutherford to Cambridge University.

Chadwick chose to attend the University of Manchester as he had not studied Latin, and enrolled in 1908. Like most students, he lived at home, walking the 4 miles (6.4 km) to the university and back each day. At the end of his first year, he was awarded a Heginbottom Scholarship to study physics. The physics department was headed by Ernest Rutherford, who assigned research projects to final year students, and he instructed Chadwick to devise a means of comparing the amount of radioactive energy of two different sources.

The idea was that they could be measured in terms of the activity of one gram (0.035 ounces) of radium, a unit of measurement which would become known as the Curie. Unfortunately, Rutherford's suggested approach was unworkable, something Chadwick knew but was afraid to tell Rutherford, so Chadwick pressed on alone, and eventually devised the required method. The results became Chadwick's first paper, which, co-authored with Rutherford, was published in 1912.

Having devised a means of measuring gamma radiation, Chadwick proceeded to measure the absorption of gamma rays by various gases and liquids. This time the resulting paper was published under his name only. He was awarded his Master of Science (MSc) degree in 1912, and was appointed a Beyer Fellow. The following year he was awarded an Exhibition Scholarship, which allowed him to study and research at a university in Continental Europe.

In his research, Chadwick continued to probe the atomic nucleus. In 1925, the concept of spin had allowed physicists to explain the Zeeman Effect, but it also created unexplained anomalies. At the time it was believed that the nucleus consisted of protons and electrons, so nitrogen, for example, with a mass number of 14, was assumed to contain 14 protons and 7 electrons. This gave it the right mass and charge, but the wrong spin.

At a conference at Cambridge on beta particles and gamma rays in 1928, Chadwick met Geiger again, who brought with him a new model of his Geiger counter, which had been improved by his post-doctoral student

Walther Müller. This was something that Chadwick had not used since the war, and the new Geiger-Müller counter was potentially a major improvement over the scintillation techniques then in use, which relied on the human eye for observation.

The major drawback with it was that it detected alpha, beta and gamma radiation, and radium, which the Cavendish laboratory normally used in its experiments, and was therefore unsuitable for what Chadwick had in mind. However, Chadwick knew that polonium was an alpha emitter, and Lise Meitner sent Chadwick about 2 mCi of this material from Germany.

In January 1939, Meitner created an uproar with a paper that explained how uranium atoms, when bombarded by neutrons, broke into two roughly equal fragments, a process they called fission. They calculated that this would result in the release of about 200 MeV, implying an energy release orders of magnitude greater than chemical reactions. It was soon noted that if neutrons were released during fission, then a chain reaction was possible. Bohr theorised that fission was more likely to occur in the uranium 235 isotope, which made up only 0.7 percent of natural uranium.

Chadwick did not believe that there was any likelihood of another war with Germany in 1939, and took his family for a holiday on a remote lake in northern Sweden. The news of the outbreak of WWII therefore came as a shock. Determined not to spend another war in an internment camp, Chadwick made his way to England by boat. In October 1939, Chadwick received a letter from Sir Edward Appleton, the Secretary of the Department of Scientific and Industrial Research, asking for his opinion on the feasibility of an atomic bomb. Chadwick responded cautiously. He did not dismiss the possibility, but carefully went over the large number of theoretical and practical difficulties involved.

The matter of cooperation on the atomic bomb had to be taken up at the highest level in the UK and US. Chadwick then began a tour of the Manhattan Project facilities in November 1943, except for the Hanford Site, which he was not allowed to visit. Observing the work in the facility at Oak Ridge, Tennessee, he realised how wrong he had been about building the plant in wartime Britain. In early 1944, he moved to Los Alamos, New Mexico with his wife Aileen and their twins, who now spoke with Canadian accents. For security reasons, he was given the cover name of James Chaffee.

By early 1945, Chadwick was spending most of his time in Washington, and his family relocated from Los Alamos to a house on Washington's Dupont Circle in April 1945. He was present at the meeting of the Combined Policy Committee on 4th July when Field Marshall Sir Henry Wilson gave Britain's agreement to use the atomic bomb against Japan. Chadwick was also present at the Trinity nuclear test on 16th July when the first atomic bomb was detonated.

Inside its core was a polonium-beryllium modulated nuclear initiator, a development of the technique that

Chadwick had used to discover the neutron over a decade before. As described by William Lawrence, the *New York Times* ace reporter, "Never before in history had any man lived to see his own discovery materialize itself with such telling effect on the destiny of man."

The final great physicist that we will discuss before turning our attention to the technological advances made during the Nazi era, and in particular the developments in gravity drive propulsion, is Werner Heisenberg.

Werner Heisenberg was a German theoretical physicist and one of the key figures in the development of quantum mechanics. He published his first major work in 1925 in a ground-breaking paper. Heisenberg was born in 1901, in Würzburg, Germany. He has been awarded both the Nobel Prize in Physics and the Max Planck Medal.

Heisenberg formulated the quantum theory of ferromagnetism, the neutron-proton model of the nucleus, the S-matrix theory in particle scattering, and various other significant breakthroughs in quantum field theory and high-energy particle physics. A prolific author, Heisenberg wrote more than 600 original research papers, philosophical essays and explanations for general audiences. His work is still available in the nine volumes of the *Gesammelte Werke* (Collected Works).

Heisenberg is synonymous with the so-called uncertainty, or indeterminacy, principle of 1927, and for one of the earliest breakthroughs in quantum mechanics in 1925. In recognition of his work on a unified field theory, the so-called "world formula", he won the Nobel Prize for Physics in 1932 at the young age of thirty-one.

Heisenberg stayed firmly in Germany during the worst years of the Hitler regime, heading Germany's research effort on the applications of nuclear fission during World War II. He also played a vital role in the reconstruction of West German science after the war. Heisenberg's role was crucial in the success of West Germany's nuclear and high-energy physics research programs.

No one better represents the plight and the conduct of German intellectuals under Hitler than Werner Heisenberg, whose task it was to build an atomic bomb for Nazi Germany. The controversy surrounding Heisenberg still rages, because of the nature of his work and the regime for which it was undertaken. Historians today are still investigating what precisely Heisenberg knew about the physics of the atomic bomb. They also ask how deep was his loyalty to the German government during the Third Reich, and assuming that he had been able to build a bomb, would he have been willing to do so?

Digging deep into the archival records among formerly secret technical reports, we have established that Heisenberg had to face the moral problem of whether he should design a bomb for the Nazi regime.

Only when he and his colleagues were interned in England and heard about Hiroshima did Heisenberg realise the full terror of this new weapon. He began at once to construct an image of himself as a "pure" scientist who could have built a bomb but chose to work on reactor design instead. Was this fiction? Many people think not. In reality, Heisenberg blindly supported and justified the cause of German victory. This is one of the 20th century's great enigmas.

Heisenberg had been captured and arrested by US Colonel Pash at Heisenberg's retreat in Urfeld, on 3rd May 1945, in what was a true alpine-type operation in territory still under the control of German forces. He was taken to Heidelberg, where, on 5th May, he met his old friend Samuel Abraham Goudsmit for the first time since the Ann Arbor visit in 1939. Germany surrendered just two days later. Heisenberg did not see his family again for eight months. He was moved across France and Belgium and flown to England on 3rd July 1945.

He was among ten top German scientists who were held at Farm Hall in England. This facility had been a safe house of the British Foreign Intelligence Service, now known as MI6. During their detention, their conversations were recorded. Conversations thought to be of intelligence value were transcribed and translated into English. The transcripts were not released until 1992.

The Americans soon realised the value of Heisenberg, and his knowledge was used during the Manhattan Project. Colonel Boris Pash reported directly to General Leslie Groves, commander of the Manhattan Engineering District, which was developing atomic weapons for the United States. The chief scientific advisor to Operation Alsos was the physicist Goudsmit. He was selected for this task because of his knowledge of physics, and because he spoke German and personally knew a number of the German scientists who worked on the Nazi nuclear energy project.

The objectives of Operation Alsos were originally to determine if the Germans had an atomic bomb program and to exploit German atomic-related facilities, intellectual materials, material resources and scientific personnel for the benefit of the US. Field personnel during the early stages of this operation generally swept into areas which had just come under the control of the Allied military forces, but sometimes they operated in areas still controlled by German forces.

Berlin had been the location of many German scientific research facilities. To limit casualties and loss of equipment, many of these facilities were dispersed to other locations in the latter years of the war. The Kaiser Wilhelm Institute for Physics had mostly been moved in 1943 and 1944 to Hechingen and its neighbouring town of Haigerloch, on the edge of the Black Forest, which eventually became the French occupation zone. This move and a little luck allowed the Americans to take into custody a large number of German scientists associated with nuclear research. The only section of the institute which remained in Berlin was the low-temperature physics section, headed by Ludwig Bewilogua, who was in charge of the exponential uranium pile.

Nine of the prominent German scientists who published reports in *Kernphysikalische Forschungsberichte* as members of the Uranverein were picked up by Operation Alsos and incarcerated in England. These scientists were Erich Bagge, Kurt Diebner, Walther Gerlach, Otto Hahn, Paul Harteck, Werner Heisenberg, Horst Korsching, Carl Friedrich von Weizsäcker and Karl Wirtz. Also incarcerated was Max von Laue, although he had nothing to do with the nuclear energy project. Goudsmit, the chief scientific advisor to Operation Alsos, thought von Laue might be beneficial to the post-war rebuilding of Germany and would benefit from the high-level contacts he would have in England.

CHAPTER 9

I believe the most significant technological development during the 1930s, which has had the most profound impact on the lives of everyone in the world, was when British scientists and engineers developed radar. By 1939, Britain had installed radar stations at many points along the coast. This gave the RAF vital warning of pending German attacks, as the aircraft could be detected while they were still assembling into formations over France.

Although the RAF was outnumbered four to one by the Luftwaffe in both warplanes and pilots in 1939, radar technology allowed the RAF to use their very limited resources to deny the Nazis air superiority over England. This subsequently resulted in Hitler having to cancel his planned invasion of Britain in 1940. This radar network was the world's first true command and control system, and this model has been implemented by virtually every other nation since.

Subsequently, the same engineers improved this system by developing centimetric radar. Centimetric radar was first fitted to British convoy escorts in 1941, and was subsequently refined and miniaturised to allow it to be fitted to aircraft during 1942. This system was so effective that it could detect the surface reflection from the periscope of a submerged U-boat at a distance of up to 15km, depending on the sea state.

The development of centimetric radar again saved our skins, as without it, the U-boat fleet would have probably won the Battle of the Atlantic. This would have prevented the massive build-up of US and Canadian military personnel and equipment in southern England, and would therefore have prevented the D-Day invasion of Normandy which changed world history forever.

Following our discussion of radar, we will look at asdic, the ultrasonic system used to detect submerged U-boats, and the development of German U-boats and their countermeasures during World War II.

Considering the technical ingenuity and huge advances that the German scientists and engineers made during World War II, I have always been baffled by why they did not produce an effective weapon against convoy escorts. Most warships at that time had substantial deck and belt armour, in order to offer some protection against shells and torpedoes. The most vulnerable part of warships was the bottom of the hull, where the steel was fairly thin.

Confirmation of this weakness was demonstrated when the British X-Craft (midget submarines) were towed to the Norwegian fjord where the battleship *Tirpitz* was hiding. The *Tirpitz* was the sister ship of the *Bismarck*, and at the time they were the most powerful battleships in the world. However, a tiny X-Craft with a four-man crew managed to penetrate the torpedo nets surrounding the *Tirpitz*, and although they did not sink her, the charges they placed beneath the hull crippled this mighty ship for six months. After being repaired, Hitler had her moved to Northern Norway, well away from Britain. However, the RAF sent a squadron of Lancaster bombers to Northern Russia to refuel, and then sank her anyway.

Following World War II, when nations realised how vulnerable surface ships were to attacks from aircraft, no more battleships were built. Today, the capital ships in most navies are aircraft carriers.

I remember back in the early 1990s, I was in Perth working on a contract for Woodside Petroleum. While I was there, the *USS Constellation* carrier battle group paid a courtesy call to the port of Fremantle at the mouth of the Swan River. The *USS Constellation* has since been decommissioned, but she was a massive and impressive ship. I went on board her and spent the entire day on a guided tour of the ship, which was fascinating. I remember the captain telling us that when a US carrier battle group showed up on someone's doorstep, only eight air forces in the world had more firepower than his single battle group.

That evening, most of the US Navy sailors were given shore leave. I remember that Fremantle and Perth looked like a new US Navy base. On the *Constellation* alone I believe there were 6,000 sailors, but there were plenty of

US Marines in full dress uniform in order to make sure that the crew behaved themselves.

The attractive young Australian Kylie Minogue wannabes flocked to the fighter pilots like bees to a honeypot. The pilots looked like Tom Cruise in their starched white uniforms, with the F-14 tomcat buckles on their belts. It was surreal, almost like being on the film set when Hollywood was making the movie *Top Gun*.

Back to the North Atlantic now. I'm sure that many of the readers have seen Wolfgang Petersen's superb film *Das Boot*, which shows both the bravery and despair of the Kriegsmarine U-boat arm in the early 1940s. The excellent film *U-571* shows the same struggle from an American perspective. If you have not seen these films, I fully recommend them, as they give a fascinating insight into World War II submarine operations.

After the U-boat had launched its attack, it submerged and then remained largely defenceless against depth-charge attacks from the escort convoys.

The Germans could have designed and installed small, vertically firing torpedoes, which could have been kept in a pod behind the conning tower. They would only have needed to be able to travel a maximum of 300 metres, and could then detonate against the bottom of the hull of a convoy escort that was depth-charging the U-boat. As the escort convoys needed to steam directly over the position of the U-boat in order to launch a depth-charge attack, small vertical-firing torpedoes could well have saved a lot of German U-boat crews. History records that out of all of the military services involved in World War II, only the Japanese kamikazes (not surprisingly) suffered worse losses than the Kriegsmarine U-boat arm. During World War II, 40,000 Germans sailors served on U-boats. Thirty thousand never came home.

Chain Home was the title given to the radar defence established in Britain in the years that led to the Battle of Britain in 1940. Chain Home, along with Chain Home Low, provided Fighter Command with its early warning system so that fighter pilots could get airborne as early as was possible to combat incoming Luftwaffe aircraft.

The original chain of RDF stations (Radio Direction Finding – the term "radar" was not adopted until 1943) consisted of twenty-one stations. They were built from Southampton to the Tyne and the first was finished at Bawdsey in 1936, which also served as a radar training school. It was handed over to the RAF in May 1937. The radar station at Dover was handed over in July 1937. Both became operational in 1938. By the start of the war, RAF aircraft had been fitted with IFF (Identification Friend or Foe), which allowed each station to know whether what they were observing was friendly or not.

Chain Home radars had the ability to detect incoming aircraft at a variety of heights and distances. Targets that flew at 1,000 feet could be detected at a distance of 25 miles. Targets that flew at 2,000 feet could be detected at a distance of 35 miles. Targets that flew at 5,000 feet could be detected at a distance of 50 miles, and targets that flew at 13,000 feet could be detected at a distance of 83 miles.

Chain Home was helped by Chain Home Low. Thirty of these smaller stations were placed either on high ground, such as the North Downs, or on the coast. Those on the coast were very open to attack, and were frequently the victims of attacks by Stuka dive-bombers. Chain Home Low used a narrow searchlight beam that was useful against low-level flights but only over a shorter distance.

Chain Home and Chain Home Low were connected by telephone, and were able to exchange information and data, as well as pass it on the Filter Room at Fighter Command. By using information from Chain Home, Chain Home Low and the Observer Corps, Fighter Command had as much information as could have been acquired in such a situation using the technology that was available.

The information provided to Fighter Command was vital. Chain Home could detect Luftwaffe squadrons as they gathered over the coast of Northern France. Chain Home Low could detect aircraft flying low enough to avoid detection by Chain Home. With such information, Fighter Command usually had about twenty minutes to put fighter squadrons in the air. Timing was vital, as both Hurricane and Spitfire pilots preferred to attack from on high, as height gave them the advantage over the enemy. A Spitfire needed thirteen minutes to scramble and then get to its preferred flying height of 20,000 feet. A Hurricane needed slightly longer, about sixteen minutes. Therefore the twenty minutes given to them by Chain Home usually allowed Fighter Command to get into a more advantageous position.

The work of scanning a cathode ray tube within a Chain Home station was done by women in the Women's Auxiliary Air Force. It was their expertise that made Chain Home a success, as the earlier they detected aircraft gathering over France, the earlier Fighter Command could assess and act on the situation. As the stations were inviting targets for Luftwaffe attacks, the work by its very nature was very dangerous.

The development of this radar system started in 1915, when Robert Watson-Watt joined the Meteorological Office, working in Aldershot in Hampshire. Over the next twenty years, he studied atmospheric phenomena and developed the use of radio signals generated by lightning strikes to map out the position of thunderstorms. The difficulty in pinpointing the direction of these fleeting signals using rotatable directional antennas led, in 1923, to the use of oscilloscopes in order to display the signals. The operation eventually moved to the outskirts of Slough in Berkshire, and in 1927 formed the Radio Research Station (RRS), Slough, an entity under the Department of Scientific and Industrial Research (DSIR). Watson-Watt was appointed the RRS Superintendent.

As war clouds gathered over Great Britain, the likelihood of air raids and the threat of invasion by air and sea drove a major effort in applying science and technology to defence. In November 1934, the Air Ministry established the Committee for Scientific Survey of Air Defence (CSSAD), with the official function of considering how far recent advances in scientific and technical knowledge could be used to strengthen the present methods of defence against hostile aircraft. Commonly called the Tizard Committee, after its Chairman, Sir Henry Tizard, this group had a profound influence on technical developments in Great Britain.

H. E. Wimperis, Director of Scientific Research at the Air Ministry and a member of the Tizard Committee, had read about a German newspaper article claiming that the Germans had built a death ray using radio signals, accompanied by an image of a very large radio antenna. Both concerned and potentially excited by this possibility, but highly sceptical at the same time, Wimperis looked for an expert in the field of radio propagation who might be able to pass judgement on the concept.

Watt, Superintendent of the RRS, was now well established as an authority in the field of radio, and in January 1935, Wimperis contacted him asking if radio might be used for such a device. After discussing this with his scientific assistant, Arnold Wilkins, Wilkins quickly produced a back-of-the-envelope calculation that showed that the energy required would be enormous. Watt wrote back that this was unlikely, but added the following comment. "My attention is being turned to the difficult problem of radio detection, and numerical considerations on the method of detection by reflected radio waves will be submitted when required".

Over the following several weeks, Wilkins considered the radio detection problem. He outlined an approach and backed it with detailed calculations of necessary transmitter power, reflection characteristics of an aircraft and needed receiver sensitivity. He proposed using a directional receiver based on Watt's lightning detection concept, listening for powerful signals from a separate transmitter. Timing, and thus distance measurements, would be accomplished by triggering the oscilloscope's trace with a muted signal from the transmitter, and then simply measuring the returns against a scale. Watson Watt sent this information to the Air Ministry on 12th February 1935, in a secret report titled *The Detection of Aircraft by Radio Methods*.

Reflection of radio signals was critical to the proposed technique, and the Air Ministry asked if this could be proven. To test this, Wilkins set up receiving equipment in a field near Upper Stowe, Northamptonshire.

On 26th February 1935, a Handley Page Heyford bomber flew along a path between the receiving station and the transmitting towers of a BBC shortwave station in nearby Daventry. The aircraft reflected the 6 MHz (49-metre) BBC signal, and this was readily detected by Doppler-beat interference at ranges up to 8 miles (13km). This convincing test, known as the Daventry Experiment, was witnessed by a representative from the Air Ministry, and led to the immediate authorisation to build a full demonstration system.

Based on pulsed transmissions as used for probing the ionosphere, a preliminary system was designed and built at the RRS by the team. Their existing transmitter had a peak power of about 1KW, and Wilkins had estimated that 100KW would be needed. Edward George Bowen was added to the team to design and build such a transmitter. Bowen's transmitter operated at 6MHz, had a pulse repetition rate of 25Hz, a pulse width of 25μs, and approached the desired power.

Orford Ness, a narrow, 19-mile (31km) peninsula in Suffolk along the coast of the North Sea, was selected as the test site. Here the equipment would be openly operated in the guise of an ionospheric monitoring station.

In May 1935, the equipment was moved to Orford Ness. Six wooden towers were erected; two for stringing the transmitting antenna, and four for corners of crossed receiving antennas. In June, general testing of the equipment began.

On 17th June, the first target was detected by a Scapa flying boat at 17 miles (27km) range. On this date, radio-based detection and ranging was demonstrated for the first time. Watson-Watt, Wilkins and Bowen are generally credited with initiating what would later be called radar.

In December 1935, the British Treasury appropriated £60,000 for a five-station system for Chain Home, covering approaches to the Thames Estuary. The secretary of the Tizard Committee, Albert Percival Rowe, coined the acronym RDF as a cover for the work, meaning Range and Direction Finding but suggesting the already well-known Radio Direction Finding.

Late in 1935, responding to Lindemann's recognition of the need for night detection and interception equipment, and realising the existing transmitters were too heavy for aircraft, Bowen proposed fitting only receivers to aircraft. In 1937 Bowen's team used their crude ASV radar, the world's first airborne set, to detect the Home Fleet in dismal weather. Only in spring 1939, "as a matter of great urgency" after the failure of the searchlight system Silhouette, did attention turn to using ASV for air-to-air interception (AI).

Demonstrated in June 1939, AI got a warm reception from Dowding, and even more so from Churchill. However, its accuracy, depending on the height of the aircraft, meant CH was not accurate enough to place an aircraft within its detection range, and an additional system was required. Its wooden chassis also had a disturbing tendency to catch fire (even with attention from expert technicians).

In 1940 John Randall and Harry Boot developed the cavity magnetron which made 10cm radar a reality. This device, the size of a small dinner plate, could be carried easily on aircraft, and the short wavelength meant the antenna would also be small, and hence suitable for mounting on aircraft. The short wavelength and high power made it very effective at spotting submarines from the air.

To aid Chain Home in making height calculations, at Dowding's request, the Electrical Calculator Type Q (commonly called the Fruit Machine) was introduced in 1940.

The solution to night intercepts would be provided by Dr W. B. Lewis, who proposed a new, more accurate ground control display, the Plan Position Indicator (PPI), a new Ground Controlled Interception (GCI) radar, and reliable AI radar. The AI sets would ultimately be built by EMI. GCI was unquestionably delayed by Watson-Watt's opposition to it and his belief that CH was sufficient, as well as by Bowen's preference for using ASV for navigation, despite Bomber Command disclaiming a need for it, and by Tizard's reliance on the faulty Silhouette system.

In March 1936 the work at Orford Ness was moved to Bawdsey Manor, nearby on the mainland. Until this time, the work had officially still been under the DSIR, but was now transferred to the Air Ministry. At the new Bawdsey Research Station, the CH equipment was assembled as a prototype. There were equipment problems when the RAF first tested the prototype station in September 1936. These were cleared by the next April, and the Air Ministry started plans for a larger network of stations.

Initial hardware at CH stations was as follows: the transmitters operated on four pre-selected frequencies between 20 and 55 MHz, adjustable within fifteen seconds, and delivered a peak power of 200 KW. The pulse duration was adjustable between 5 to 25μs, with a repetition rate selectable as either 25 or 50Hz. For synchronisation of all CH transmitters, the pulse generator was locked to the 50 Hz of the British power grid. Four 360-foot (110-metre) steel towers supported transmitting antennas, and four 240-foot (73-metre) wooden towers supported cross-dipole arrays at three different levels. A goniometer was used to improve the directional accuracy from the multiple receiving antennas.

By the summer of 1937, twenty initial CH stations were in operation. A major RAF exercise was performed before the end of the year, and was such a success that £10million was appropriated by the Treasury for an eventual full chain of coastal stations. At the start of 1938, the RAF took over control of all CH stations, and the network began regular operations.

In May 1938, Rowe replaced Watson-Watt as Superintendent at Bawdsey. In addition to the work on CH and the successor systems, major work was now being performed in airborne RDF equipment. This was led by E. G. Bowen and centred on 200MHz (1.5 metre) radio sets. The higher frequency allowed smaller antennas, appropriate for aircraft installation.

From the initiation of RDF work at Orford Ness, the Air Ministry had kept the British Army and the Royal Navy generally informed. This led to both of these forces having their own RDF developments. We will now look at the development of ASDIC, a scientific breakthrough that played a major part in the success of the Battle of the Atlantic.

ASDIC was the primary underwater detection device used by the Allied convoy escort ships throughout World War II. The first crude versions were created towards the end of World War I, and further developed in the following years by the Royal Navy.

ASDIC, known to the Americans as sonar, was basically a transmitter-receiver sending out a highly directional sound wave through the water. If the sound wave struck a submerged object it was reflected back and picked up by the receiver. The length of the time from transmission until the echo was received was used to measure the range, which was shown as a flickering light on the range scale. By mounting the transmitter head so that it could be directed almost like a searchlight, the bearing of the target could be read from the compass receiver.

The transmitter (sound) head extended beneath the ship, and was encased in a large metal dome to minimise the noise of the water rushing past the ship while at moderate speed. This dome was filled with water, through which the sound passed, although this water was stationary and acted almost like a bumper. Noise levels remained relatively low at moderate speeds, but anything above 18 knots resulted in too much noise, and good contacts were difficult to find. The same problems also resulted from bad weather when the ships were rolling, pitching and heaving.

During screening operations, the ASDIC operator searched through an arc of roughly 45 degrees each side of the base course of the vessel. The ASDIC had to be stopped at regular intervals on this arc for long enough to allow the relatively slow underwater sound waves to return should they locate a submerged target. Normally the head would be stopped on a bearing and a sound pulse would be transmitted, which would be heard as a "ping" noise. If no echo was received after several seconds the head would be rotated a few degrees (usually five), and the process repeated throughout the watch.

If the outgoing impulse stuck a submerged target, the echo would be heard as a distinct "beep". If this occurred, the ASDIC operator would sound the alarm, feed the range and bearing to the bridge, and then immediately start left and right cuts to try to determine the width of the target and try to see if it was moving from one side to another. He could also determine if the target was closing or opening the range.

Echoes would bounce back from many things besides the U-boats, such as whales, schools of fish, vertical sea currents and ship's wakes. This caused many false alarms, especially with inexperienced operators. The veteran operator was much better at figuring out these bad signals and hunting down the intended target. The commanding officers quickly learned which operators were the most reliable.

Another problem was that often a real U-boat could not be detected due to water conditions. ASDIC was not very reliable in rough water, nor when layers of different temperature deflected the sound waves. U-boats could dive beneath such layers to avoid detection. Modern nuclear and diesel submarines use this tactic to this day.

The device could also be used to listen as well as pinging. The propeller noises of the U-boat would sometimes be heard, as well as the noises from the operation of various types of machinery on board, such as its use of the compressed air in the ballast tanks to change depths. This detection method was unusual, as one of the standard German tactics, when located, was to dive deep, rig for silent running and hide beneath a thermal layer at speeds slow enough to eliminate any cavitation from the propellers.

When the U-boat was located, the attacking vessel would rush directly towards the contact, usually at a speed of 15 knots. This run was used to determine the final movements of the target, and to further plot the final attack. The attacking vessel had to be fairly sure where the U-boat was, and estimate where it would be when the depth charge reached its calculated depth. Thus the attacking vessel would have to take a lead on the U-boat, much as a hunter does on a bird. At 500 metres the Allied commander hoped to know what the U-boat was doing, and then he finalised his attack.

As the range closed, the U-boat would pass under the beam of the ASDIC and be lost to the escort. The deeper the U-boat was, the longer the range of the lost contact was, and it was thus more difficult to attack accurately. Normally a good and firm contact was lost at 300 metres. This did not affect the forward-launched Hedgehogs as much as the depth charges.

Even if the attack was delivered with the correct lead angle and firing time, there was no guarantee of damage to the U-boat since its depth could differ from the settings at which the depth charges were set to explode. The correct depth of the U-boat could only be guessed or estimated based on the range at which contact was lost.

The U-boats, of course, used tactics to evade the depth charges and Hedgehogs. The best time to act was when the attacking vessel had taken its lead angle and the ASDIC contact was just lost.

A very common German move was to run away from the escort and force it on a stern chase, pinging through the wake of the U-boat, which could give the ASDIC a hard time. Then at the moment of the ASDIC losing contact, the U-boat would take a radical turn to the left or right, and more often than not escape out of the attacking pattern.

Another tactic was to turn radically with great power and disturb the water in order to confuse the ASDIC, and sometimes causing the attacker to be shaken off. The

Germans also often released chemical pellets, which would produce clouds of bubbles to reflect the sound waves of the ASDIC.

Yet another tactic was to dive very deep, under a thermal layer or beneath the depth at which depth charges were normally set to explode. From 1942 onwards, depths of 200 meters (over 600 feet) were not uncommon in an evasive tactic.

CHAPTER 10

While writing this book, I asked some friends to proof read various sections. A good friend of mine, who is a retired English teacher from Melbourne, made me laugh, as he said that I must be careful not to turn the book into an autobiography. I commented that I was simply trying to include some amusing incidents that have happened to me during my life in order to lighten the heavier scientific parts of the book.

He then told me about the rumours of Mick Jagger's autobiography. He said that some years ago, Mick Jagger was allegedly paid £50,000 as an initial down payment for his memoirs. He was not required to actually write anything himself, as the publisher provided him with a ghost writer. After six months, so the story goes, not a word had been written, and the publisher asked for the money back. The ghost writer was then allowed to interview Mick, but gave up. When asked about his early life, he allegedly said that it all started in the 1960s. "Keith said try a bit of this, and then I got out of the taxi this morning".

Following our discussion of radar and ASDIC, we will finish this section covering the struggle in the Atlantic convoy lanes by looking at the development of the U-boat during the 1940s. I believe that during the German arms build-up in the 1930s, one of Hitler's major mistakes was to concentrate his resources in large single assets such as the *Bismarck* and *Tirpitz*. Admiral Karl Dönitz had argued repeatedly for an increase in the strength of his U-boat fleet.

Many U-boats could be built for the same cost, in terms of both money and resources, as the cost of building a single huge battleship. Also, a single U-boat with a fifty-man crew is capable of destroying a battleship with a crew of 2,000 or more, as the Royal Navy discovered early in World War II in Scapa Flow. Had Hitler listened to Dönitz, the Battle of the Atlantic may have been very different. However, following the sinking of the *Bismarck*, Hitler realised that wolf packs were considerably more effective than a single battleship, and U-boat production increased at a great rate from this point onwards.

Irrespective of how good your battleship is, and the Germans arguably had the best, they were still no match for the Royal Navy's fleet. This was simply because they could be attacked by several Royal Navy battleships at the same time, splitting the firepower of the Nazi vessel and making its escape very unlikely.

In addition, the Nazis had no aircraft carriers, and the ability of the Royal Navy to launch carrier-borne aircraft in the mid-Atlantic was a major factor in the sinking of the *Bismarck*.

Although Dönitz eventually got his own way with new resources being poured into U-boat production, he also made some serious errors of judgement himself. Soon, his strengthened Atlantic U-boat fleet started to suffer increasing losses. This was primarily due to ASDIC, which he was aware of, but also to the centimetric radar fitted to the convoy escorts, which he was not aware of. When this CR was miniaturised and fitted to Allied aircraft, the U-boat losses mounted still further. Unknown to Dönitz and the Nazis, the British at Bletchley Park had also cracked the Enigma naval encryption code. The Germans blamed the increasing losses on the activities of spies.

During World War II, U-boat warfare was the major component of the Battle of the Atlantic, which lasted the duration of the war. Germany had the largest submarine fleet in World War II, since the Treaty of Versailles had limited the surface navy of Germany to six battleships (of less than 10,000 tons each), six cruisers and twelve destroyers. Prime Minister Winston Churchill wrote "The only thing that really frightened me during the war was the U-boat peril."

In the early stages of the war, the U-boats were extremely effective in destroying Allied shipping, initially in the mid-Atlantic, where there was a large gap in air cover. There was an extensive trade in war supplies and food across the Atlantic, which was critical for Britain's survival. Later, when the United States entered the war, the U-boats ranged from the Atlantic coast of the United States and Canada to the Gulf of Mexico, and from the Arctic to the west and southern African coasts and even as far east as Penang. The US military engaged in various tactics against German incursions in the Americas. These included military surveillance of foreign nations in Latin America and the Caribbean, in order to deter any local governments from supplying German U-boats.

Because speed and range were severely limited underwater while running on battery power, U-boats were required to spend most of their time surfaced running on diesel engines, diving only when attacked or for rare daytime torpedo strikes. The more ship-like hull design reflects the fact that these were primarily surface vessels which had the ability to submerge when necessary. This contrasts with the cylindrical profile of modern nuclear submarines, which are more hydrodynamic underwater (where they spend the majority of their time) but less stable on the surface. Indeed, while U-boats were faster on the surface than submerged, the opposite is generally true of modern subs. The most common U-boat attack during the early years of the war was conducted on the surface and at night. This period, before the Allied forces developed truly effective antisubmarine warfare (ASW) tactics, was referred to by German submariners as "die glückliche Zeit" or "the happy time".

The U-boats' main weapon was the torpedo, though mines and deck guns (while surfaced) were also used. By the end of the war, almost 3,000 Allied ships (175 warships and 2,823 merchant ships) had been sunk by U-boat torpedoes. Early German World War II torpedoes were straight runners, as opposed to the homing and pattern-running torpedoes which were fielded later in the war. They were fitted with one of two types of pistol trigger. The impact trigger detonated the warhead upon contact with a solid object, and the magnetic trigger detonated upon sensing a change in the magnetic field within a few meters.

One of the most effective uses of magnetic triggers would be to set the torpedo's depth to just beneath the keel of the target. The explosion under the target's keel would create a shock wave, and the ship could break in two. In this way, even large or heavily armoured ships could be sunk or disabled with a single well-placed hit. In practice however, the depth-keeping equipment and magnetic and contact exploders were notoriously unreliable in the first eight months of the war. Torpedoes would often run at an improper depth, detonate prematurely or fail to explode altogether, sometimes bouncing harmlessly off the hull of the target ship.

This was most evident in Operation Weserübung, the invasion of Norway, where various skilled U-boat commanders failed to inflict damage on British transports and warships because of faulty torpedoes. The faults were largely due to a lack of testing. The magnetic detonator was sensitive to mechanical oscillations during the torpedo run, especially at high latitudes, due to fluctuations in the Earth's magnetic field. These were eventually phased out, and the depth-keeping problem was solved by early 1942.

Later in the war, Germany developed an acoustic homing torpedo, the G7/T5. It was primarily designed to combat convoy escorts. The acoustic torpedo was designed to run straight to an arming distance of 400 meters and then turn toward the loudest noise detected. This sometimes ended up being the U-boat itself. At least two submarines may have been sunk by their own homing torpedoes. Additionally, it was found these torpedoes were only effective against ships moving at greater than 15 knots (28 km/h). Subsequently, the Allies countered acoustic torpedoes with noise-making decoys such as the Foxer, FXR, CAT and Fanfare. The Germans in turn countered this by introducing newer and upgraded versions of the acoustic torpedoes, like the late-war G7ES, and the T11 torpedo. However, the T11 did not see active service.

U-boats also adopted several types of "pattern-running" torpedoes which ran straight out to a pre-set distance, then travelled in either a circular or ladder-like pattern. When fired at a convoy, this increased the probability of a hit if the weapon missed its primary target.

During World War II, the Kriegsmarine produced many different types of U-boats as technology evolved. Most notable was the Type VII, known as the workhorse of the fleet, which was by far the most produced type. Type IX boats were larger and specifically designed for long-range patrols, some travelling as far as Japan and the east coast of the United States. With the Type XXI "Elektroboot", German designers realised the U-boat depended on submerged ability both for combat effectiveness and survival. This was the first submarine whose design favoured submerged performance. The Type XXI featured a revolutionary streamlined hull design, which was used as the basis for the later *USS Nautilus* nuclear submarine.

Its propulsion system featured a large battery capacity, which allowed it to cruise submerged for long periods and reach unprecedented submerged speeds. A larger battery was possible because the space it occupied was originally intended to store hydrogen peroxide for a Walther turbine, which was unsuccessful on the Type XVII. The type XXI U-boat developed the basic hydrodynamic design which almost all modern submarines have adopted.

Throughout the war an arms race evolved between the Allies and the Kriegsmarine, especially in the area of detection and counter-detection. Advancements in British radar were countered by U-boats being fitted with radar warning receivers, to give them some time to dive before the enemy closed in. However, soon the Allies switched to centimetric radar which rendered the radar detectors ineffective. U-boat radar systems were also developed, but many captains chose not to utilise them for fear of broadcasting their position to enemy patrols.

The Germans took the idea of the Schnorchel (snorkel) from captured Dutch submarines, though they did not begin to implement it on their own boats until rather late in the war. The Schnorchel was a retractable pipe which supplied air to the diesel engines while submerged at periscope depth, allowing the boats to cruise and recharge their batteries while maintaining a degree of stealth. It was far from a perfect solution, however.

There were problems with the device's valve sticking shut or closing as it dunked in rough weather. Since the system used the entire pressure hull as a buffer, the diesels would instantaneously suck huge volumes of air from the boat's compartments, and the crew often suffered painful ear injuries. Waste disposal was a problem when the U-boats spent extended periods without surfacing. Speed was limited to 8 knots (15 km/h), lest the device snap from stress. The Schnorchel also had the effect of making the boat essentially noisy and deaf in sonar terms. Finally, Allied radar eventually became sufficiently advanced that the Schnorchel mast itself could be detected beyond visual range.

The later U-boats were covered in a sound-absorbent rubber coating to make them less of an ASDIC target. They also had the facility to release a chemical bubble-making decoy, known as Bold, after the mythical kobold.

The British had a major advantage in their ability to read the German naval Enigma codes. An understanding of the German coding methods had been brought to Britain via France from Polish code breakers. Thereafter, code books and equipment were captured by raids on German weather ships and from captured U-boats. A team at Bletchley Park worked constantly to break new German codes as they were introduced. The speedy decoding of messages was vital in directing convoys away from wolf packs, and allowing interception and destruction of U-boats. This was demonstrated when the Naval Enigma machines were altered in February 1942, and wolf pack effectiveness greatly increased until the new code was broken.

The German submarine *U-110*, a Type IXB, was captured in 1941 by the Royal Navy, and its Enigma machine and documents were removed. *U-559* was also captured by the British in October 1942. Three British sailors boarded her as she was sinking, and desperately threw all the code books out of the submarine. Two of them, Able Seaman Colin Grazier and Lieutenant Francis Anthony Blair Fasson, continued to throw code books out of the ship as it went underwater, and went down with it. Further code books were captured by raids on weather ships. *U-744* was boarded by crew from the Canadian ship *HMCS Chilliwack* on 6th March 1944, and codes were taken from her, but by this time in the war most of the information was known. The *U-505,* a Type IXC, was captured by the United States Navy in June 1944. It is presently a museum ship at the Museum of Science and Industry in Chicago.

Two other events in the battle took place in 1942, when German U-boats attacked four Allied ore carriers at Bell Island, Newfoundland. The carriers *SS Saganaga* and *SS Lord Strathcona* were sunk by *U-513* on 5th September 1942, while the *SS Rosecastle* and *PLM 27* were sunk by *U-518* on 2nd November, with the loss of sixty-nine lives. When the submarine launched a torpedo at the loading pier, Bell Island was to become the only location in North

America to be subject to direct attack by German forces in World War II.

Operation Deadlight was the code name for the scuttling of U-boats surrendered to the Allies after the defeat of Germany near the end of the war. Of the 154 U-boats that surrendered, 121 were scuttled in deep water off Lisahally, Northern Ireland or Loch Ryan, Scotland in late 1945 and early 1946.

From 1955, the West German Bundesmarine was allowed to have a small navy. Initially two sunken Type XXIIIs and a Type XXI were raised and repaired. In the 1960s, West Germany re-entered the submarine business. Because Germany was initially restricted to a 450-tonne displacement limit, the Bundesmarine focused on small coastal submarines to protect against the Soviet threat in the Baltic Sea. The Germans sought to use advanced technologies to offset the small displacement, such as non-magnetic steel to protect against naval mines and magnetic anomaly detectors.

The initial Type 201 was a failure because of hull-cracking problems. The subsequent Type 205, first commissioned in 1967, was a success, and twelve were built for the German Navy. To continue the U-boat tradition, the new boats received the classic "U" designation starting with the *U-1*.

With the Danish government's purchase of two Type 205 boats, the German government realised the potential for the submarine as an export. Three of the improved Type 206 boats were sold to the Israeli Navy, becoming the Gal-class. The German Type 209 diesel-electric submarine was the most popular export sales submarine in the world from the late 1960s into the first years of the 21st century. With a larger 1,000-1,500 tonne displacement, the class was very customisable and has seen service with fourteen navies, with fifty-one examples being built as of 2006.

Germany has brought the U-boat name into the 21st century with the new Type 212. The 212 features an air-independent propulsion system using hydrogen fuel cells. This system is safer than previous closed-cycle diesel engines and steam turbines, cheaper than a nuclear reactor, and quieter than either. While the Type 212 is also being purchased by Italy, the Type 214 has been designed as the follow-on export model, and has so far been sold to Greece, South Korea and Turkey.

CHAPTER 11

Following our discussion of the advances in U-boat technology, we will now turn our attention to the wartime developments that produced arguably the greatest advance in science during the last century – the development of gravity drive propulsion systems.

While researching this book, the author has read many articles by various people giving many pages of information on the subject of the Nazi development of flying discs. However, each article seems to be a rehash of another article or book previously compiled by someone else. During this research, I have not found any proper scientific analysis of the principles that have the capacity to make this type of propulsion system a reality.

I have seen no credible independent analysis of advances made in this area in the second half of the 20th century, and in particular no scrutiny or analysis of patents that have already been filed to cover developments in this area. I think that this is probably because the authors of the various pieces had very little knowledge of classical physics, let alone quantum field physics or string theory.

They probably thought that the cost of employing an eminent physics professor to evaluate such data would be prohibitive. In addition, they were probably attempting to write articles and books that were more sensational rather than investigative or factual. The only exception in my experience has been the work performed by the British investigative journalist and author Nick Cook. We will discuss our initial meeting, subsequent communications and his research in a later section.

For completeness, I will now briefly recap both the facts and rumours of the 1940s developments in this field. However, I know that the principle of the reported work is factual. I have seen what others apart from myself have achieved using rotating superconductors and other devices. These developments have mostly been achieved with a six-figure budget and just a few technicians. The Kammler group, the first to develop this technology, had an almost unlimited budget, and many of the best brains in the world.

By the end of 1943, Kammler was in sole control of all of the advanced Nazi scientific research, engineering and manufacturing in the Third Reich. His group, known as the Kammler stab, was probably the most secretive organisation within the entire Nazi regime. On several occasions, Hitler boasted about his wonder weapons, soon to be introduced, although at the time people assumed these to be the V2 rockets, Me 262 jet fighters and similar projects that were visible. There were far greater technical advances under development.

During the Allied advance through France and into Germany during 1944 and 1945, the Allies, and in particular the Americans, sent Secret Service and technical investigation personnel, who arrived directly behind the front line troops, in order to interrogate anyone of interest in the recently-liberated areas. It was not until this time that the Western Allies had any idea of the pending technical capabilities of the Nazis, or of the secret structure of the research and development programmes themselves.

The author believes that the disappearance of Kammler and the bulk of his new technology was orchestrated following the information stumbled upon by these intelligence units early in 1945. Although there is no definitive proof, and rumours of Kammler's death were circulated at the time, the circumstantial evidence that has been documented makes the case for his final assisted exit from Germany compelling.

Firstly, on 15th April 1945, the US Third Army under the command of General George Patton met up with the Soviet Red Army at the River Elbe. This effectively cut Germany in half, and everyone at the time expected that the US and Soviet forces would jointly move north in order to capture Berlin, and share the glory of taking the capital of the Third Reich. What actually happened was rather different.

The Americans generously informed the Soviets that they could head north alone, and have the glory of taking Berlin.

General Patton was instructed to start a "mop-up operation" in Southern Germany. The Russians gratefully accepted, and Patton took several armoured divisions in a headlong rush south. His target was the Skoda works at Pilsen in Czechoslovakia. US intelligence had learnt that this was where much of Kammler's research was performed.

Time was of the essence for the Americans. The Third Reich was on the brink of collapse, and very soon this area would fall into the agreed Soviet area of control. When the first division of Patton's Third Army arrived at Pilsen, they surrounded and looted everything in the Pilsen Skoda works. This reportedly ran to sixteen trucks full of documents and other material. Further information and equipment was recovered from nearby abandoned mines, after the staff at the Skoda works were interrogated by US forces.

When the Soviets learned of Patton's escapades, a major diplomatic storm erupted. The Americans withdrew from Pilsen with their prize, but by this time the Soviets already suspected what the US Third Army had been doing there. Eight days later, after a profound apology from the US, the Americans handed over "all" (I think not) of the materials that they had seized. Although this did defuse the situation, the Soviets had no way of knowing what was in the Skoda works in the first place, so could not accuse the Americans of cherry-picking this technology before the remainder of the spoils were returned.

Despite extensive research, the author knows of no strategic reason why Patton was directed south to make a beeline for Pilsen, and then withdraw again, thereby achieving no strategic advantage at all. The only credible reason was to loot the technology of the Kammler Group.

The second compelling piece of circumstantial evidence is the fact that Kammler, despite holding the third most senior position within the SS, was only ever mentioned twice at the Nuremberg Trials. The trials were controlled by the US, and although many SS officers holding far lower ranks were tried and sentenced to death, Kammler was barely mentioned. Even some low-ranking officers who had evaded capture were tried in absentia and the death sentence was handed out.

It is also a matter of historical record that in April 1945, intercepted Enigma transmissions from Himmler instructed Kammler to send a Junkers JU-390 to Berlin. The Junkers JU-390 was a six-engine long-range transport aircraft, and it is believed that only three were ever produced. Incredibly, Kammler then told Himmler (who was still the top commander in the SS) that no plane was available at the moment. This plane had the range to fly directly from Germany to anywhere in the Americas, and also to half of Asia should the pilots be instructed to do so. The next day, two Junkers JU-390s and Kammler disappeared off the radar forever.

For the author, the most compelling piece of circumstantial evidence was the window-dressing and deception surrounding the arrival of Wernher von Braun in the US. His image had now been polished to be Dr von

Braun, a very talented engineer from Germany, as opposed to SS Major von Braun. Using a skilful piece of PR, the Americans got away with this. However, Kammler was a completely different kettle of fish.

He was a cornerstone in the development of the final solution and the Nazi death camps. He personally oversaw the design of many of these camps, and also improved the efficiency of the body disposal in the camp's crematoria. Kammler was implicated up to his neck in the final solution, and admitting to the American public that he was now in the United States was just not an option. When Kammler evacuated "the Bell" (the major component of his gravity drive development) from the secret SS research facility in Wenceslas Mine in 1945, the entire team of over sixty scientists who had been working on the project were reportedly murdered by the SS.

On examining all of the evidence that is available today, many people, the author included, believe that Kammler managed to bargain with American intelligence, in order that his war crimes would be swept under the carpet in return for his vast horde of advanced technology. Kammler would almost certainly have died from old age by now, but I think that it is a racing certainty that his remains lie in an unmarked grave somewhere in the United States.

There was a remarkable explosion in technological advances in the US over the following decades. However, one of the most prized and secretive developments was the B-2 bomber. The design of this flying wing stealth plane is an almost exact copy of the airframe of the Horten brothers' Ho-229 stealth bomber that was designed almost half a century earlier.

The Horten Ho-229 and Northrup Grumman B-2 stealth bombers are about as similar as the Anglo-French Concorde airliner and the Russian copy dubbed "Concordeski". Do the Russians have anything similar? No – they should have gone to Pilsen first.

We will look at the other known developments of the Kammler group later in this section, but will now return to the Bell, which was allegedly the jewel in the crown of the Kammler group's achievements.

In "UFOlogy", conspiracy theory, science fiction and comic book stories, claims or stories have circulated linking UFOs to Nazi Germany. The German UFO theories describe supposedly successful attempts to develop advanced aircraft or spacecraft prior to and during World War II, and further assert the post-war survival of these craft in secret underground bases in Antarctica or South America.

According to the limited available information on the UFOs, various classifications of Nazi UFO craft such as Rundflugzeug, Feuerball, Diskus, Haunebu, Heuneburg Geate and Vril-Kugelblitz (not related to the self-propelled anti-aircraft gun of the same name) have all been referenced. Accounts appear as early as 1950, likely inspired by historical German development of specialised engines such as Viktor Schauberger's "Repulsine" around the time of World War II. Elements of these claims have been widely incorporated into various works of fiction. German UFO literature very often conforms largely to documented history on the following points:

The Third Reich claimed the territory of New Swabia in Antarctica, sent an expedition there in 1938, and planned others.

The Third Reich conducted research into advanced propulsion technology, including rocketry, Viktor Schauberger's engine research, flying wing aircraft and the Arthur Sack AS-6 experimental circular winged aircraft.

Some UFO sightings during World War II, particularly those known as foo fighters, were thought by the allies to be prototype enemy aircraft designed to harass Allied aircraft through electromagnetic disruption, a technology similar to today's electromagnetic pulse (EMP) weapons.

In World War II, the so-called foo fighters and a variety of other unusual and anomalous aerial phenomena were witnessed by both Axis and Allied personnel. While some foo fighter reports were dismissed as the misperceptions of troops in the heat of combat, others were taken seriously, and leading scientists such as Luis Alvarez began to investigate them. In at least some cases, Allied intelligence and commanders suspected that foo fighters reported in the European theatre represented advanced German aircraft or weapons. This seemed credible, given that the Germans had already developed such technological innovations as V-1 and V-2, and the first jet engine fighter plane.

Similar sentiments regarding German technology resurfaced in 1947 with the first wave of flying saucer reports after Kenneth Arnold's widely reported close encounter with nine crescent-shaped objects moving at a high velocity. Personnel of Project Sign, the first US Air Force UFO investigation group, noted that the advanced flying wing aeronautical designs of the German Horten brothers were similar to some UFO reports. Later in 1959, Captain Edward J. Ruppelt, the first director of Project BlueBook (Project Sign's follow-up investigation) wrote: "When WWII ended, the Germans had several radical aircraft and guided missiles under development."

While these early speculations and reports were limited primarily to military personnel, the earliest assertion of German flying saucers in the mass media appears to have been an article which appeared in the Italian newspaper *Il Giornale d'Italia* in early 1950. Written by Professor Giuseppe Belluzzo, an Italian scientist and a former Italian Minister of National Economy under the Mussolini regime, it claimed that "types of flying discs were designed and studied in Germany and Italy as early as 1942." Belluzzo also expressed the opinion that "some great power is launching discs to study them".

The Bell was among the first flying objects to be connected with the Nazis. It apparently had occult markings on it, and it was also rumoured to have been very similar to a Wehrmacht document about a vertical take-off aircraft. It is directly related to the supposed crash of a bell-shaped object that occurred in Kecksburg, Pennsylvania, USA in December 1965. The same month, German engineer Rudolf Schriever gave an interview to German news magazine *Der Spiegel* in which he claimed that he had designed a craft powered by a circular plane of rotating turbine blades 49 feet (15 meters) in diameter.

He said that the project had been developed by him and his team at the Skoda works near Prague until April 1945, when he fled Czechoslovakia. His designs for the disk and a model were stolen from his workshop in Bremerhaven-Lehe in 1948, and he was convinced that Czech agents had built his craft for a foreign power. In a separate interview with *Der Spiegel* in October 1952 he said that the plans were stolen from a farm he was hiding in near Regen on 14th May 1945. There are other discrepancies between the two interviews that add to the confusion. However, many sceptics have doubted that such a Bell was actually designed or ever built.

In 1953, when Avro Canada announced that it was developing the VZ-9-AV Avrocar, a circular jet aircraft with an estimated speed of 1,500 mph (2,400 km/h), German engineer Georg Klein claimed that such designs had been developed during the Third Reich. Klein identified two types of supposed German flying discs; the first a non-rotating disc developed at Breslau by V-2 rocket engineer Richard Miethe, which was captured by the US. Miethe also fled to the US via France and ended up working for Avro. The second consisted of a ring of revolving discs around a fixed cockpit. Klein claimed that he had witnessed this craft's first manned flight on 14th February 1945, when it managed to climb to 12,400 metres (40,700 feet) in three minutes, and attained a speed of 2,200 km/h (1,400 mph) in level flight.

Aeronautical engineer Roy Fedden remarked that the only craft that could approach the capabilities attributed to flying saucers were those being designed by the Germans towards the end of the war. Fedden was also the chief of the technical mission to Germany for the Ministry of Aircraft Production.

The Bell was reported to be around 9 feet in diameter, and 12 to 14 feet in height. When in operation, it consumed large amounts of electrical power and reportedly glowed with a violet-blue haze surrounding the equipment due to the ionisation of the air in the vicinity.

Inside the Bell, two contra-rotating drums were installed. Norwegian-born physicist Rolf Widerøe wrote in his autobiography about the development of the Bell at Hamburg by the company CHF Muller. In his patent, his diagrams show one sphere inside another spun on a common axis. A vacuum was then created to propagate plasma inside the evacuated chambers.

Within the Bell, it was reported that heated mercury vapour would have been injected, and then, once spun up to speed, subjected to powerful discharges of electricity in order to ionise the mercury vapour. Under this influence, the mercury would fluoresce, and photons would collide with extremely energetic electrons, creating X-rays and gamma rays. This process was said to stimulate a mysterious compound known "Xerum 525" to produce the effects that were then observed.

The Nazis were known to have made a special paraffin from deuterium, which was thought to have been used within the Bell. The reports of the violet colour of the Xerum 525 were supposedly due to the Red Mercury within this compound. According to the US intelligence propaganda today, Red Mercury does not exist. It is however advertised for sale on the Internet by major Russian nuclear facilities for very large sums of money.

Up until 1944, the Nazi Bell was located in an underground facility close to the Polish city of Wrocław. The final location for the Bell's development was at the Wenceslas mine, situated in a remote valley close to a large power station. The mining operations in the area produced the coal for the power station, and the remoteness, availability of substantial electrical power, and the old mine workings made the Wenceslas mine an ideal location for the unobserved development of this technology.

According to some reports, additional substances were said to be employed in the experiments, referred to as Leichtmetalle (light metal), with thorium and beryllium peroxides. Some describe Die Glocke (the Bell) as emitting strong radiation when activated, an effect that supposedly led to the death of several unnamed scientists and various plant and animal test subjects. Based upon certain external indications, the Polish investigator Witkowski states that the ruins of a concrete framework aesthetically dubbed "The Henge" in the vicinity of the Wenceslas mine (50°37'43"N 16°29'40"E) may have once served as a test rig for an experiment in "anti-gravity propulsion" generated with Die Glocke. However, the derelict structure itself has also been interpreted to resemble the remains of a conventional industrial cooling tower. Witkowski's statements and views prompted further conjecture about this device from various American authors.

Since 1945, much has been written about Nazi flying discs and the Bell, and more recently many entire books written covering UFOs and flying saucers. The author believes the majority of these works to be mostly fictitious, but there is undoubtedly some factual basis to some of the accounts related. Some people have even gone so far as suggesting that the Bell was developed to investigate time travel.

As time has progressed, it has become more difficult to separate the wheat from the chaff. I believe that today all we can say with certainty is that the propulsion systems that are required to propel such craft can be built, but precisely what the Bell was used for is still a matter of conjecture.

In the final analysis however, we know for certain that whatever the purpose of the Bell was, it disappeared along with Kammler in 1945, and the Germans considered this device so important that every one of the dozens of scientists who had ever worked on this project were shot by the SS and buried in a mass grave.

CHAPTER 12

During World War II, the Nazis developed the V-1 flying bomb. Although it was far from perfect, it was arguably the world's first effective cruise missile. Also known as the buzz bomb or doodlebug, it was an early pulse jet-powered predecessor of the modern cruise missile.

The V-1 was developed at the Peenemünde Research Centre by the Luftwaffe. During initial development it was known by the codename "Cherry Stone". The first of the so-called vengeance weapons (Vergeltungswaffen) designed for the terror bombing of London, the V-1 was fired from launch sites along the French and Dutch coasts. The first V-1 was launched at London on 13th June 1944, one week after (and prompted by) the successful Allied landings in Normandy. At its peak, more than one hundred V-1s a day were fired at south-east England, and 9,521 in total. This rate decreased as the launch sites were overrun, until October 1944, when the last V-1 site in range of Britain was finally taken by Allied forces. This caused the remaining V-1s to be directed at the port of Antwerp and other targets in Belgium, with a further 2,448 V-1s being launched. The attacks stopped when the last site was overrun on 29th March 1945.

The British operated an arrangement of defences (including guns and fighter aircraft) to intercept the bombs before they reached their targets, as part of Operation Crossbow, while the launch sites and underground V-1 storage depots were the targets of strategic bombing.

The history of the V-1 began in the late autumn of 1936. While employed by the Argus Company, Fritz Gosslau began work on the further development of remote-controlled aircraft. Argus had already developed remote-controlled surveillance aircraft such as the AS 292 (military designation FZG 43).

On 9th November 1939, a proposal for a remote-controlled aircraft carrying a payload of 1,000 kg (2,200lbs) over a distance of 500 km (310 miles) was forwarded to the RLM (German Air Ministry). Argus joined with Lorentz AG and Arado Flugzeugwerke to develop the project as a private venture. In April 1940, Gosslau presented an improved study of the project to the RLM, known as Project P-35.

On 31st May, Rudolf Bree of the RLM commented that he saw no chance that the projectile could be deployed in combat conditions, as the proposed remote control system was seen as a design weakness. Heinrich Koppenberg, a director of Argus, met with Ernst Udet on 6th January 1941 to try to convince him that the development should be continued, but Udet opted to cancel it.

Despite this, Gosslau was convinced that the basic idea was sound and proceeded to simplify the design. As an engine manufacturer, Argus lacked the capability to produce a fuselage for the project, and Koppenberg sought the assistance of Robert Lusser, chief designer and technical director at Heinkel. On 22nd January 1942, Lusser took up a position with the Fieseler aircraft company. He met with Koppenberg on 27th February and was informed of Gosslau's project. Gosslau's design used two pulse jet engines. Lusser improved the design to use a single engine.

A final proposal for the project was submitted to the Technical Office of the RLM on 5th June and the project was renamed Fi 103, as Fieseler was to be the chief contractor. On 19th June, General Erhard Milch gave the Fi 103 production a high priority, and development was undertaken at the Luftwaffe's Erprobungsstelle coastal test centre at Karlshagen, part of the Peenemünde-West facility.

By 30th August, Fieseler had completed the first fuselage, and the first flight of the Fi 103 took place on 10th December, when it was air-dropped by an FW 200.

The V-1 was designed with a fuselage constructed mainly of welded sheet steel, and wings built of plywood. The simple Argus-built pulse jet engine pulsed at fifty times per second, and the characteristic buzzing sound gave rise to the colloquial names.

Ignition of the Argus pulse jet was accomplished using an automotive-type spark plug located behind the intake shutters, with current supplied from a portable starting unit. Three air nozzles in the front of the pulse jet were at the same time connected to an external high-pressure air source which was used to start the engine. Acetylene gas was typically used for starting, and very often a panel of wood or similar material was held across the end of the tailpipe to prevent the fuel from diffusing and escaping before ignition. The V-1 was fuelled with 150 gallons of 75 octane gasoline.

Once the engine had been started and the temperature had risen to the minimum operating level, the external air hose and connectors were removed, and the engine's resonant design kept it firing without any further need for the electrical ignition system.

It has been stated that the V-1's Argus As 014 pulse jet engine needed a minimum airspeed of 150 mph (240 km/h) to operate. The Argus As 014 (also known as a resonant jet) could in fact operate at a lower airspeed due to the nature of its intake shutters and its acoustically-tuned resonant combustion chamber.

The minimum air speed was probably needed due to the very high stall speed of the small wings. The V-1 could not take off under its own power, and thus required to either be ground-launched with power assistance using a ramp, or air-launched from a modified bomber aircraft such as the Heinkel He-111. Beginning in January 1941, the V-1's pulse jet engine was also tested on a variety of craft, including an experimental attack boat known as the "Tornado". The unsuccessful prototype was a version of a Sprengboot, in which a boat loaded with explosives was steered towards a target ship, and the pilot would leap out of the back at the last moment. The Tornado was assembled from surplus seaplane hulls connected in a catamaran-like fashion, with a small pilot cabin on the crossbeams. The Tornado prototype was a noisy underperformer and was abandoned.

The V-1 guidance system used a simple autopilot to regulate altitude and airspeed, developed by Askania in Berlin. Although the original design plan of using a radio-control system would have allowed for precision attacks, the guidance system adopted instead allowed the missile to be used against very large targets, such as London. A weighted pendulum system provided fore-and-aft stabilisation to control pitch, which was also damped by a gyrocompass. Operating power for the gyroscope platform and the flight control actuators was provided by two large spherical compressed air tanks which also pressurised the fuel tank. These air tanks were charged to 150 bar before launch. With a nose-mounted counter determining how far the missile would fly, it was only necessary to launch the V-1 with the ramp pointing in the correct direction, and the autopilot then controlled the flight.

There was a more sophisticated interaction between yaw, roll and other parameters. A gyrocompass (set by swinging in a hangar before launch) gave feedback to control the dynamics of pitch and roll. The gyroscope remained true on the basis of feedback received from a magnetic compass, and from the fore-and-aft pendulum. This interaction meant that rudder control was sufficient for steering, and no banking mechanism was needed.

In a V-1 which landed in March 1945, without detonating, between Tilburg and Goirle in the Netherlands, several issues of the German wartime propaganda newspaper *Signal* were found inserted into the left wing's tubular steel spar. They were assumed to have been added for weight to pre-set the missile's static equilibrium before launching. It is also known that several of the first buzz bombs to be launched were provided with a small radio transmitter (using a triode valve marked "S3", but equivalent to a then-current power valve, type RL 24T1), to check the general direction of flight related to the launching place's and the target's grid coordinates by radio bearing.

An odometer driven by a vane anemometer on the nose determined when the target area had been reached, accurately enough for area bombing. Before launch, the counter was set to a value that would reach zero upon arrival at the target in the prevailing wind conditions. As the missile flew, the airflow turned the propeller, and every thirty rotations of the propeller counted down one number on the odometer. This counter triggered the arming of the warhead after about 60 km (37 miles). When the count reached zero, two detonating bolts were fired. These caused two spoilers on the elevators to be released; the linkage between the elevators and servo was jammed, and a guillotine device cut off the control hoses to the rudder servo. These actions put the V-1 into a steep dive. While this was originally intended to be a power-dive, in practice the dive caused the fuel flow to cease, which stopped the engine. The sudden silence after the buzzing alerted people to the impending impact.

The conventional launch sites could theoretically launch about fifteen V-1s per day, but this rate was difficult to achieve on a consistent basis. The maximum rate achieved was eighteen. Overall, only about twenty-five percent of the V-1s hit their targets. The majority were lost because of a combination of defensive measures, mechanical unreliability or guidance errors. With the capture or destruction of the launch facilities used to attack England, the V-1s were employed in attacks against strategic locations in Belgium, primarily the port of Antwerp.

The intended operational altitude was originally set at 2,750 metres (9,000 feet). However, repeated failures of a barometric fuel pressure regulator led to it being changed in May 1944, halving the operational height, thereby bringing V-1s into far easier range of the guns used by Allied AA units.

The trial versions of the V-1 were air-launched. Most operational V-1s were launched from static sites on land, but from July 1944 to January 1945, the Luftwaffe launched approximately 1,170 V-1s from modified Heinkel He 111s of the Kampfgeschwader 3 (third Bomber Wing, the so-called "Blitz Wing") flying over the North Sea. Apart from the obvious motive of permitting the bombardment campaign to continue after static ground sites on the French coast were lost, air-launching gave the Luftwaffe the opportunity to outflank the increasingly effective ground and air defences put up by the British against the missile.

In order to minimise the associated risks (primarily radar detection), the aircrews developed a tactic called "lo-hi-lo". The He 111s would, upon leaving their airbases and crossing the coast, descend to an exceptionally low altitude. When the launch point was neared, the bombers would swiftly ascend, fire their V-1s, and then rapidly descend again to the previous "wave-top" level for the return flight. Research after the war estimated a forty percent failure rate of air-launched V-1s. Also, the He-111s used in this role were extremely vulnerable to British night fighter attack, as the launch lit up the area around the aircraft for several seconds.

We will now look at the underground facilities created by the Nazis during the second half of World War II. Due to the extensive Allied bombing of German factories and infrastructure, it was decided to move all of the vital and sensitive industrial and research facilities underground. To accomplish this, Kammler used the slave labour at his disposal to create hundreds of tunnels and galleries at many locations within mountains in order to protect his projects.

Most of these tunnels were excavated in the Harz Mountain region of Northern Germany. The Mittelwerk and the Nordhausen area housed the largest of these complexes. They were used for the manufacture of the V-2 rocket and Me 262 jet fighter, although the location of the latter site was given away by the runway built on the mountain top. However, these underground facilities also protected Nazi research into nuclear reactors and atomic weapon development.

The author believes that this particular topic has also been the subject of severe misrepresentation and disinformation by the Allies since 1945. The British and Americans maintain to this day that the only nuclear facilities the Germans had were very rudimentary research establishments, and the Nazis were a long way from developing a practical nuclear reactor, let alone building a nuclear weapon.

In view of the disinformation they later put out regarding Russian nuclear technology, the history of SS officers that the US needed and many other subjects on which they were later caught out, the assessment of the Nazi nuclear capability recorded by Western history is disinformation bordering on being completely fictitious.

Firstly, Germany had some of the finest technical brains and physicists in the world during this period. Physicists such as Max Planck, Werner Heisenberg and Erwin Schrödinger developed quantum field theory, and were all Nobel Physics Laureates. To even suggest that men of this towering intellectual calibre were not capable of building a working nuclear reactor or bomb is quite absurd.

The Germans were also enriching uranium long before 1945. The German chemical giant IG Farben had constructed an enormous facility outside Berlin. The cover story was that this facility was built to produce synthetic rubber. However after many years of operation, and having consumed a good part of the entire electrical power generated for the Berlin region, not a single kilogram of synthetic rubber is recorded as having been produced there. Corroborating evidence comes from many employees who confirmed that this facility actually housed thousands of high-speed centrifuges enriching uranium.

IG Farben is notorious for its role in the Holocaust. The company was formed in 1925 from a number of major chemical companies that had been working together closely since World War I. During its heyday, IG Farben was the largest chemical company in the world and the fourth largest overall industrial concern, after General Motors, US Steel and Standard Oil of New Jersey.

Following the Nazi takeover of Germany, IG Farben became involved in numerous war crimes during World War II. Most notoriously, the firm's pro-Nazi leadership openly and knowingly collaborated with the Nazi government to produce the large quantities of Zyklon B necessary to gas to death millions of Jews and other "undesirables" at various extermination camps during the

Holocaust. The firm ceased operating following the fall of Nazi Germany in 1945, when the company was seized by the Allies. Its assets were utterly liquidated in 1952, and many executives were imprisoned (and several executed) at the Nuremberg Trials for their roles in the atrocities.

Engulfed by lawsuits and universal condemnation after the war's end, the company itself no longer exists. Before the company went defunct it was merely as an asset-less shell with the sole stated goal of continuing to do business so it may pay many millions of dollars in reparations to the families of the victims of its many crimes.

Further evidence of the Nazi nuclear capability came at the end of the war in Europe with the surrender of the Nazi U-boat *U-234*. Unfortunately for the Americans and British, her cargo manifests were published in the press as they were considered to be fairly insignificant. Many of the crates and heavy cylinders on board this U-boat were marked *U-235*. The ill-informed military censors just assumed that they must have been due for dispatch on a different U-boat. It later transpired that the cylinders contained enriched uranium 235, believed to have been produced as part of the German atomic bomb programme, and on its way to Japan. However by then the cat was out of the bag. Again, this cannot possibly be reconciled with the Allied claims of Nazi nuclear development and their nuclear technology.

A number of people also believe that in fact the Allies were extremely lucky that the war in Germany ended in

May 1945. Several have suggested that it would have been just a matter of a few more months until this uranium had been turned into a working bomb, in which case London may well have been the first city to suffer a nuclear attack instead of Hiroshima. It has further been suggested that this Nazi uranium was used by the Americans in their own atomic bomb programme. Again, the truth regarding this will probably never be known.

The Mittelwerk was incorporated as a private company on 24th September 1943, and received a contract for the production of 12,000 V-2s (which will be discussed in the next section). After meeting with Hitler on 18th August, SS Chief Heinrich Himmler informed armaments minister Albert Speer that he was personally taking over V-2 production, and placing SS General Hans Kammler in charge of the Mittelwerk complex. It was Kammler who had been in charge of the building of the extermination camps and gas chambers at Auschwitz-Birkenau, Maidenek and Belzec.

The Mittelwerk tunnel system consisted of two parallel main tunnels, A and B, each roughly 6,200 feet (1.17 miles) long, bent in a shallow "S" curve, and connected at various points by a regular series of cross-tunnels like the rungs of a ladder. The cross-tunnels (called Halls, or Kammer) were about 600 feet long (from the outside wall of Tunnel A to the outside wall of Tunnel B), and were numbered from 1 to 46, beginning at the north side of the mountain. Tunnels A and B had a height of 21 to 23 feet, and a width of 29 to 36 feet.

The Halls were somewhat smaller in cross-section, but still the underground space was vast, estimated to be over a million square feet.

The southern entrance of Tunnel A and Halls 46 through 43 were devoted to V-1 production, in what was called Mittelwerk II. V-2 assembly (Mittelwerk I) occupied Halls 21 through 42, while the northern end of the tunnel complex (Halls 1 through 20) was dedicated to Junkers aircraft engine production in what was called the Nordwerk.

Each of the main tunnels had two sets of regular-gauge railroad tracks running through it. In general, Tunnel A was used to transport parts and materials for the V-2 into the factory and for storage. The Halls were used for assembling, testing and stocking subassemblies for the rockets. Tunnel B served as the primary assembly line, which began at Hall 21 and moved south towards Hall 42, covering a distance of some 2,300 feet (about four tenths of a mile) and carrying rockets out of the Mittelwerk. Many of the Halls contained offices for the German draftsmen, engineers and foremen (called Meisters), who directed the detainees. Niches and cul-de-sac chambers were hollowed out of the main tunnels, and also halls for additional storage.

The two tracks in Tunnel B formed parallel assembly lines. V-2s to be assembled would be placed on pairs of four-wheeled railroad bogies connected by a beam, and moved from north to south. At each stage of the line, additional parts were added to the assemblies, until the completed rockets arrived at Hall 41 on the south end.

This hall, which had been excavated well below the regular floor level of the main tunnels, was over 50 feet high and contained a huge spanning crane, enabling the rockets to be erected vertically. One whole side of Hall 41 contained a series of multi-level vertical inspection scaffolds for the rockets. This was necessary because final fluid and gyroscopic tests (among others) could not be carried out on a horizontal rocket.

The general assembly process went as follows. First, the centre section of the rocket (the fuselage with its two huge alcohol and liquid oxygen tanks) was assembled. Next, the propulsion group (combustion chamber, turbine pump and air bottles) was attached. Then, the tail section of the rocket, with its propulsion ring, rudder servos and fins, was attached to the motor. Finally, the guidance compartment (the control amplifier, electrical distribution panel, main time switch, radio equipment etc.) was attached to the front of the missile, and the completed rocket went for final testing and delivery to the launching batteries. Warheads were transported separately and attached to the rockets in the field.

V-2 parts however were never designed to be fully interchangeable. Combustion chambers, fuel pumps and many valves had to be matched up to each other, and specifically tested and regulated for each missile. This meant that each V-2 engine assembly had to be test-fired prior to final assembly. Wernher von Braun was in charge of these final acceptance tests. On 4th August 1943, Peenemünde made the decision that V-2 production would be carried out for the most part using concentration camp labour, in a ratio reported to have been set at ten to fifteen detainees to every German worker. The SS, which ran the camps, became the supplier and organiser of V-2 production manpower. A small concentration camp was in fact located in the basement of Building F1 at the base.

The rocket's design demanded close tolerances for parts. Given the diversity of sources and subcontractors for the various components, and the state of disruption prevailing in the German economy due to Allied bombing, a lot of the work in the tunnels consisted of inspection and re-inspection of parts and subassemblies. Many of the prisoners worked in areas devoted to filing, re-machining or otherwise tweaking various subsystems.

In April 1945, the spearhead of the advancing American troops, Combat Command B (CCB) of the 3rd Armoured Division, entered Nordhausen. Here CCB was to pause and link up with the 104th Infantry (Timber Wolf) Division before continuing its drive to the east.

Third Armoured had been warned by Army Intelligence to "expect something a little unusual" in the Nordhausen area, but they knew nothing of the horrors soon to be discovered. One of the first sickening encounters took place at the Boelcke-Kaserne (also called the Nordhausen

Camp), a former German military barracks that the SS had used as a dumping ground for prisoners from Mittelwerk camps who were too weak or diseased to include in the forced marches out of the area. The dead also included prisoners killed in an Allied bombing raid aimed at Nordhausen. An estimated 1,300 to 2,500 corpses were found there, along with a few survivors, cared for by the 104th Division's medical staff.

CHAPTER 13

Apart from the Bell, for which the known facts are sketchy, the V-2 was the most ground-breaking piece of Nazi technology of which we know the full story. The V-2 was the world's first ever ballistic missile. There was no defence against it once it was launched, and it was way ahead of anything that the Allies could produce at the time. Ironically, more people died in the manufacture of this missile than it ever managed to kill when in operation.

The initial research and testing of the V-2 was carried out close to the V-1 facility. By late 1941, von Braun's team possessed the technologies essential to the success of the V-2 (which was known as the A-4 at that time). The four key technologies for the V-2 were large liquid-fuel rocket engines, supersonic aerodynamics, gyroscopic guidance and control rudders in the exhaust stream, as it would climb outside of the Earth's atmosphere. At the time, Adolf Hitler was not particularly impressed by the V-2. He pointed out that it was merely an artillery shell with a longer range and much higher cost.

The original assembly line was set up on the lower floor of Building F1. This line was the precursor of the rail-borne horizontal transport type of assembly later used at the Mittelwerk.

On the night of 17–18th August 1943, the Allies mounted a massive air raid on Peenemünde. This raid forced the Germans to move the entire V-weapon manufacturing capability to the Mittelwerk.

In early September 1943, von Braun promised the Long Range Bombardment Commission that the V-2 development was practically concluded, but even by the middle of 1944, a complete V-2 parts list was still unavailable. By this time Hitler was sufficiently impressed by the enthusiasm of its developers, and also needed a "wonder weapon" to maintain German morale, so he authorised its deployment in large numbers.

The V-2 used a seventy-five percent ethanol/twenty-five percent water mixture for fuel, and liquid oxygen for the oxidiser. After launch the V-2 propelled itself for up to sixty-five seconds on its own power, and the guidance system controlled the pitch to the specified angle at engine shutdown, after which the rocket continued on a ballistic free-fall trajectory. The rocket reached a height of 80km (50 miles) after shutting off the engine. The fuel and oxygen pumps were steam turbines, the steam being produced by concentrated hydrogen peroxide with sodium permanganate catalyst. Both the alcohol and oxygen tanks were made from an aluminium-magnesium alloy.

The combustion chamber reached a temperature of 2,500–2,700°C (4,500–4,900°F). The alcohol-water fuel was pumped along the double wall of the main combustion chamber. This regenerative cooling both heated the fuel and cooled the combustion chamber. The fuel was then pumped into the chamber through 1,224 nozzles, which assured the correct mixture of alcohol and oxygen at all times.

Small holes also permitted some alcohol to escape directly into the combustion chamber, forming a cooled boundary layer that further protected the wall of the chamber, especially at the throat where the chamber was narrowest. The boundary layer alcohol ignited in contact with the atmosphere, accounting for the long, diffuse exhaust plume. By contrast, post-V-2 engine designs that did not employ this alcohol boundary layer cooling show a translucent plume with shock diamonds in their exhaust.

The V-2 was guided by four external rudders on the tail fins, and four internal graphite vanes at the exhaust exit of the motor. The LEV-3 guidance system consisted of two free gyroscopes (a horizontal and a vertical) for lateral stabilisation, and a PIGA accelerometer to control engine cut-off at a specified velocity. The V-2 was launched from a pre-surveyed location, so the distance and azimuth to the target were known. Fin number one of the missile was aligned to the target azimuth.

Some early V-2 tests used "guide beams" – radio signals transmitted from the ground to keep the missile on course – but the first operational models used simple analogue computers that adjusted the azimuth for the rocket, and the flying distance was controlled by the timing of the engine cut-off. The rocket then stopped accelerating, and soon reached the top of the approximately parabolic flight curve.

By February 1942 the engineers had documented the radio interference area of a V-2 as 10,000 meters around the firing point, and the first successful V-2 flight on 3rd October 1943 used radio control. Hitler commented on 22nd September 1943 that, "It is a great load off our minds that we have dispensed with the radio guiding-beam. Now no opening remains for the British to interfere technically with the missile in flight."

The painting of the operational V-2s was mostly a camouflaged ragged pattern with several variations, but at the end of the war a plain olive-green rocket also appeared. During tests, the rocket was painted in a characteristic black-and-white chessboard pattern, which aided in determining if the rocket was spinning around its longitudinal axis.

Two test launches were recovered by the Allies. These were the Backeboe rocket which landed in Sweden on 13th June 1944, and one recovered by the Polish resistance on 30th May 1944 from Blizna and transported to the UK during Operation Most III.

Test launches of V-2 rockets were made at Blizna and Tuchola Forest, and after the war, at Cuxhaven by the

British, White Sands Proving Grounds, Cape Canaveral and Kapustin Yar. Various design issues were identified and solved during V-2 development and testing. These were primarily:

- To reduce tank pressure and weight, high-flow turbo pumps were used to boost pressure.
- A short and lighter combustion chamber without burn-through was developed by using centrifugal injection nozzles, a mixing compartment and a converging nozzle to the throat for homogeneous combustion.
- Film cooling was used to prevent burn-through at the nozzle throat.
- Relay contacts were made more durable to withstand vibration and prevent thrust cut-off just after lift-off.
- Ensuring that the fuel pipes had tension-free curves reduced the likelihood of explosions at 1,200–1,800 metres (4,000–6,000 feet). Fins were shaped with clearance to prevent damage as the exhaust jet expanded with altitude.
- To control trajectory at lift-off and supersonic speeds, heat-resistant graphite vanes were used as rudders in the exhaust jet.

After Hitler's 29th August 1944 declaration to begin V-2 attacks as soon as possible, the offensive began on 8th September 1944 with a single launch at Paris, which caused modest damage near Porte d'Italie. Two more launches then followed, including one from The Hague against London on the same day. At 6:43 pm, the first landed at Chiswick, killing sixty-three-year-old Mrs Ada

Harrison, three-year-old Rosemary Clarke and Sapper Bernard Browning, on leave from the Royal Engineers. Upon hearing the double-crack of the supersonic rocket (London's first ever), Duncan Sandys and Reginald Victor Jones looked up from different parts of the city and exclaimed, "That was a rocket!", and a short while after the double-crack, the sky was filled with the sound of a heavy body rushing through the air.

As the V-2 explosions came without warning, the British government initially attempted to conceal their cause (surely not) by blaming the damage on a series of defective gas mains! However the public was not fooled, probably due to rocket fins etc. being found near the craters, and soon began referring to the V-2s as "flying gas pipes". The Germans themselves finally announced the V-2 on 8th November 1944 and only then, on 10th November 1944, did Winston Churchill inform Parliament, and the world, that England had been under rocket attack "for the last few weeks".

The positions of the German launch units did change a number of times. For example, Artillerie I-444 arrived in the south-west Netherlands (in Zeeland) in September 1944. From a field near the village of Serooskerke, five V-2s were launched on 15th and 16th September, with one more successful and one failed launch on the 18th. That same day, a transport carrying a missile took a wrong turn and ended up in Serooskerke itself, giving a villager the opportunity to surreptitiously take some photographs of the weapon. These were then smuggled to London by the

Dutch Resistance. After that the unit moved to Gaasterland in the north-west Netherlands, to ensure that the technology did not fall into Allied hands. From Gaasterland, V-2s were launched against Ipswich and Norwich from 25th September (London being out of range). Because of their inaccuracy, these V-2s did not hit their target cities. Shortly after that, only London and Antwerp remained as designated targets, as ordered by Adolf Hitler himself. Antwerp was targeted during the period of 12th to 20th October, after which time the unit moved to the Hague.

An estimated 2,754 civilians were killed in London by V-2 attacks, with another 6,523 injured, which is two people killed per V-2 rocket. However, this understates the potential of the V-2, since many rockets were misdirected and exploded harmlessly. Accuracy increased over the course of the war, particularly on batteries where the latest Leitstrahl Guide Beam apparatus was installed. Missile strikes were often devastating, causing large numbers of deaths; 160 civilians were killed and 108 seriously injured in one explosion on 25th November 1944 in mid-afternoon, when a V-2 hit Woolworth's department store in New Cross, south-east London.

After these deadly results, British intelligence spread more disinformation saying that the rockets were over-shooting their London targets by 10 to 20 miles (16 to 32km). This tactic worked, and for the remainder of the war most V-2s landed on less heavily populated areas in Kent due to erroneous recalibration. The final two rockets exploded on 27th March 1945. One of these was the last V-2 to kill a British civilian. She was Mrs Ivy Millichamp, aged thirty-four, killed in her home in Kynaston Road, Orpington in Kent.

Antwerp, Belgium was also the target for a large number of V-weapon attacks from October 1944 through March 1945, leaving 1,736 dead and 4,500 injured in greater Antwerp. Thousands of buildings were damaged or destroyed as the city was struck by 590 direct hits. The largest loss of life in a single attack came on 16th December 1944, when the roof of a crowded cinema was struck, leaving 567 dead and 291 injured.

A scientific reconstruction carried out in 2010 demonstrated that the V-2 creates a crater 20m wide and 8m deep, ejecting approximately 3,000 tons of material into the air.

Although the V-2 was an enormous technological achievement, in the final assessment it was probably not the best use of the German resources. The V-2 consumed a third of Germany's fuel alcohol production and major portions of other critical technologies. To distil the fuel alcohol for one V-2 launch required 30 tonnes of potatoes at a time when food was becoming scarce. Due to a lack of explosives, concrete was used, and sometimes the warhead contained photographic propaganda of German citizens who had died in Allied bombing.

The V-2 lacked a proximity fuse, so it could not be set for airburst, but buried itself in the target area before or just as the warhead detonated. This reduced its effectiveness. Furthermore, its early guidance systems were too primitive to hit specific targets and its costs were approximately equivalent to four-engine bombers. They were more accurate (though only in a relative sense), had longer ranges, carried many more warheads and were reusable. Moreover, the V-2 diverted resources from other, more effective programmes.

That said, the limiting factor for German aviation after 1941 was always the availability of high-octane aviation fuel (not planes or pilots), so criticisms of the V-1 and V-2 programmes that compare their cost to hypothetical increases in fighter or bomber production are misguided. Nevertheless, the weapon had a considerable psychological effect because, unlike bombing planes or the V-1 Flying Bomb (which made a characteristic buzzing sound), the V-2 travelled faster than the speed of sound, and gave no warning before impact. There was no effective defence, and no risk of pilot and crew casualties.

In comparison, in one twenty-four-hour period during Operation Hurricane, the RAF dropped over 10,000 tons of bombs on Brunswick and Duisburg, roughly equivalent to the amount of explosives that could be delivered by 10,000 V-2 rockets.

With the war all but lost, regardless of the factory output of conventional weapons, the Nazis resorted to V-weapons as a tenuous last hope to influence the war (hence Antwerp as a V-2 target), as an extension of their desire to "punish" their foes, and most importantly to give hope to their supporters with their miracle weapons. If the V-2 had no effect on the outcome of the war, its value was in its ingenuity, which set the stage for the next fifty years of ballistic military rocketry, culminating in the ICBMs of the Cold War and in the beginnings of modern space exploration.

Following the defeat of the Nazis, Operation Paperclip recruited German engineers and transported the captured V-2 rockets and parts to the United States. At the close of World War II, over 300 rail cars filled with assorted V-2 parts, including engines, fuselages, propellant tanks, gyroscopes and associated equipment were brought to the rail yards in Las Cruces, New Mexico, so they could be placed on trucks and driven to the White Sands Proving Grounds, also in New Mexico.

In addition to V-2 hardware, the US Government delivered German mechanisation equations for the V-2 guidance, navigation and control systems, as well as for advanced development concept vehicles, to US defence contractors for analysis. In the 1950s, some of these documents were useful to US contractors in developing direction cosine matrix transformations and other inertial navigation architecture concepts that were applied to early US programmes such as the Atlas and Minuteman guidance systems, as well as the Navy Submarine Inertial Navigation System.

A committee was formed with military and civilian scientists to review payload proposals for the help to tackle skill shortages in the oil industry.

alliance involves ... and Gas Acade- ... Engineering Con- ... dustry Training ... ly.

... nent aims to en- ... of industry fund- ... h operators and

contractors and promote collaborative working on the design and development of new learning products and services for the UK industry.

Opito is an industry funded, employer-led organisation committed to developing

ECTB invests around £2million a year in training and apprenticeship programmes.

During 2008, it will recruit 1,000 apprentices.

The Offshore Contractors' Association and Oil and Gas UK will be involved in a steering committee that will guide the work of the alliance partners. The committee will es-

lifestyle event at Aberdeen Exhibition and Conference Centre.

Mr Doig said: "This agreement is based on a genuine intent for both organisations to work harmoniously for the benefit of the industry and add real tangible value for employers.

"It is also for employers to help the partnership under-

will be projects to:
● Increase the flow of people into the industry.
● Create more direct routes for developing new and existing personnel.
● Ensure the industry has a range of qualifications transferable across sectors.

David Doig, chief executive of Opito, and David Edwards, chief executive of ECITB, will

Mr Edwards said: The changing business models within the industry mean that more alignment is needed to address the skill priorities.

"Working together will make this happen more quickly and effectively while ensuring duplication of effort and cost is eliminated over time."

crucial to Europe's development, but faced enormous bureaucratic obstacles. It said a new plan – the Small Business Act for Europe – would mean less late payment of invoices, access to more help with finance, innovation and training, lower VAT for services supplied locally and better access to contracts. The commission: is now urging EU governments and MEPs to give the package of measures swift approval.

Unsecured creditors unlikely to get paid

The joint liquidator o north-east constructior firm Country Life Estate (CLE), which crashed in April 2005 with estimated debts of more than £2mil lion, said yesterday it wa very unlikely there would b any funds for distribution tc unsecured creditors.

Neil Armour of profes sional services firm KPMC said net funds in hand at the end of May amounted to jus £89,077. He said there hac been delays in resolving one or two property issues, anc the last was still to be re solved. He added that h would expect the liquida tion to close shortly.

Pub chain boost for north-east producers

A Fife-based pub chain ha said food producers it Grampian will benefit from its purchasing policy.

Gastro Taverns feature numerous using farm-fresl food purchased, where pos sible, within a 40 mile radiu of its outlets.

It has recently expandec into the north-east, havin, opened the Gas Lamp ca, bar in Aberdeen's Marke Street and bought the Quo! ters Lounge at Newtonhill near Stonehaven.

ATTRACTION: Mike Bennett . . . a 50% reduction in fuel consumption would save British Airways alone more than £1billion annually. Photograph Colin Rennie

Figure A

... ey are very angry ... Some have been ... ut holding unof- ... such as downing ... platforms.

... an't support un- ... n, if it happened ... es squarely at the ... e and no one else.

... vice firm Cape ... action, a North

M HAS Y DEAL

ers ools ea

Franc blame

ATTRACTION: Mike Bennett ... a 50% reduction in fuel consumption would save British Airways alone more than £1billion annually. Photograph: Colin Rennie

New turbine could save aviation industry billions

GEOPHYSICIST SAYS SUPERCONDUCTING DEVICE COULD CUT FUEL CONSUMPTION IN HALF

BY IAN FORSYTH

AN ABERDEEN entre-
preneur revealed yesterday
that he had developed a
superconducting turbine
which he believes could save
the aviation industry hundreds of millions of pounds in
fuel costs.
Mike Bennett built his
model on a small budget,
mostly from components salvaged from ex-medical and

military equipment. He said
that, when fully developed,
the cost of the turbine would
probably be too high for cars
and other surface transport,
but its application in the aviation industry could be significant.
The geophysicist added: "I
believe that, if fitted to aircraft, fuel savings of up to
50% could be achieved when
compared to the consump-
tion of conventional turbine

engines. A 50% reduction in
fuel consumption would, for
example, save British Airways
alone more than £1billion annually on its fuel bills, in addition to the environmental
benefits of avoiding the need
to burn some 3million tonnes
of jet fuel.
"The commercial attraction
of a superconducting turbine
is therefore clear."
Mr Bennett said his tech-
nology was now ready for

commercial development,
but the costs were such that
he needs financial backing.
The entrepreneur gradu-
ated from Manchester University in 1979 with joint honours degrees in physics and
geology.
After five years working in
the oil industry, he founded
his first company in 1984.
This business adapted new
technologies to help solve
reservoir engineering prob-

lems and maximise oil and
gas recovery.
He added: "We applied
techniques and equipment
normally only used by re-
search physicists and used
them to solve problems in the
real world.
"After building up the company over 12 years, I sold it on
in 1996. I now work part-time
as a consultant, in order to
have more time to pursue my
other interests."

Figure B

INTELLECTUAL
PROPERTY OFFICE

Patents Form 1
Patents Act 1977 *(Rule 12)*

Request for grant of a patent

Concept House
Cardiff Road
Newport
South Wales
NP10 8QQ

Application number

1.	Your reference	P118034.GB.01
2.	Full name, address and postcode of the applicant or of each applicant	GENERAL TURBINE TECHNOLOGIES LIMITED 7 QUEENS TERRACE ABERDEEN AB10 1XL Aberdeenshire United Kingdom
	Patents ADP number *(if you know it)*	
3.	Title of the invention	DEVICE FOR MOVING A MASS AND/OR GENERATING A FORCE EFFECTIVE FOR MODIFYING THE GRAVITATIONAL FIELD BETWEEN MASSES AND A METHOD THEREOF
4.	Name of your agent *(if you have one)*	Murgitroyd & Company
	"Address for service" to which all correspondence should be sent. This may be in the European Economic area or Channel Islands (see warning note below) *(including the postcode)*	Murgitroyd & Company Scotland House 165-169 Scotland Street Glasgow G5 8PL Strathclyde United Kingdom
	Patents ADP number *(if you know it)*	1198015
5.	Priority declaration: Are you claiming priority from one or more earlier-filed patent applications? If so, please give details of the application(s)	

Country	Application number	Date of filing	Date available on PDAS
6. Divisionals etc: Is this application a divisional application, or being made following resolution of an entitlement dispute about an earlier application. If so, please give the application number and filing date of the earlier application		Number of earlier UK application	Date of filing *(day / month / year)*
7. Inventorship: (Inventors must be individuals not companies)			
Are all the applicants named above also inventors?	**No**		
8. Are you paying the application fee with this form?	**No**		

Figure C

Patents Form 1

9. Accompanying documents: please enter the number of
   pages of each item accompanying this form

   Continuation sheets of this form

Description:	15
Claim(s):	5
Abstract:	1
Drawing(s):	5

   If you are not filing a description, please give details of
   the previous application you are going to rely upon

Country	Application number	Date of filing	Date available on PDAS

10. If you are also filing any of the following, state how many
    against each item.

Priority documents:	0
Statement of inventorship and right to grant of a patent (Patents Form 7):	0
Request for search (Patents Form 9A):	0
Request for a substantive examination (Patents Form 10):	0
Any other documents (please specify):	

11. I/We request the grant of a patent on the basis of this application.

Signature:	Subject: GB, Murgitroyd & Company, J. Brown 12895; Issuer: , European Patent Office, European Patent Office CA	Date:	25 Mar 2011

12. Name, e-mail address, telephone, fax and/or mobile number, if any, of a contact point for the applicant	Brown, Mr. James D Email: james.brown@murgitroyd.com Telephone: +44 1224 706616 Fax: +44 141 307 8401

Warning

After an application for a patent has been filed, the Comptroller will consider whether publication or communication of the invention should be prohibited or restricted under section 22 of the Patents Act 1977. You will be informed if it is necessary to prohibit or restrict your invention in this way. Furthermore, if you are resident in the United Kingdom and your application contains information which relates to military technology, or would be prejudicial to national security or the safety of the public, section 23 of the Patents Act 1977 prohibits you from applying for a patent abroad without first getting written permission from the Office unless an application has been filed at least 6 weeks beforehand in the United Kingdom for a patent for the same invention and either no direction prohibiting publication or communication has been given, or any such direction has been revoked. Until such time or until the revocation of any direction, for any such application the address for service referred to at part 4 above must be in the United Kingdom.

Although you may have an address for service in the Channel Islands, any agent instructed to act for you must reside or have a place of business in the European Economic Area or Isle of Man.

(REV DEC07)   **Patents Form 1(e)**

Figure D

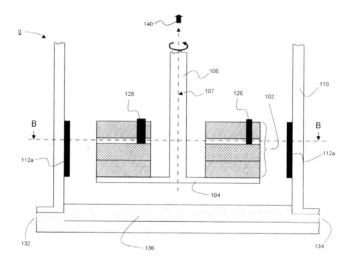

Figure E

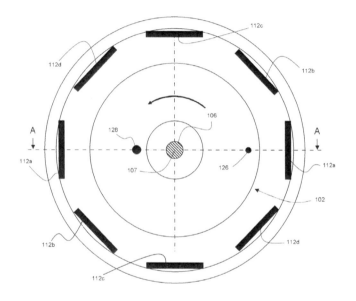

Figure F

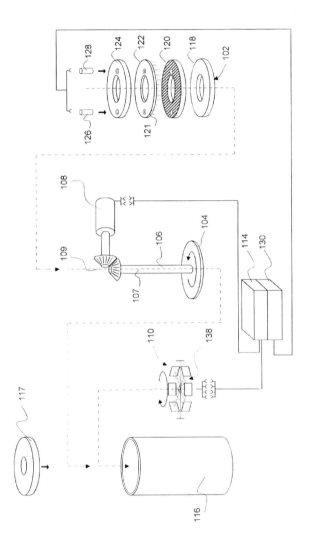

Figure G

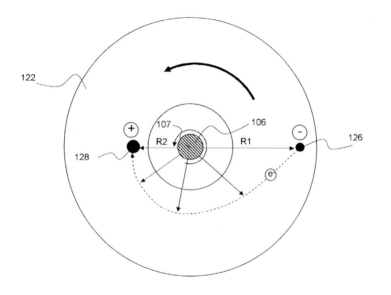

Figure H

reassembled V-2 rockets. This led to an array of experiments that flew on V-2s, and paved the way for American-manned space exploration. Devices were sent aloft to sample the air at all levels to determine atmospheric pressures and to see what gases were present. Other instruments measured the level of cosmic radiation. The first photo from space was taken from a V-2 launched by US scientists on 24th October 1946.

Only sixty-eight percent of the V-2 trials were considered successful. The Navy attempted to launch a German V-2 rocket at sea. One test launch from the aircraft carrier *USS Midway* was performed on 6th September 1947 as part of the Navy's Operation Sandy. The test launch was a partial success, as the V-2 splashed down in the ocean only 10km (6 miles) from the carrier. This launch was notable as it used foldaway arms to prevent the missile from falling over. The arms pulled away just after the engine ignited, releasing the missile. The setup may look similar to the R-7 launch procedure, but in the case of the R-7, the trusses hold the full weight of the rocket, rather than just reacting to side forces. The US Redstone rocket is a direct descendant of the V-2.

CHAPTER 14

Superconductivity is a phenomenon of exactly zero electrical resistance and the expulsion of magnetic fields occurring in certain materials when cooled below a characteristic critical temperature.

Superconductivity was discovered in 1911 by Heike Onnes, who was studying the resistance of solid mercury at cryogenic temperatures using the recently produced liquid helium as a coolant. At the temperature of 4.2K, he observed that the electrical resistance abruptly disappeared. In the same experiment, he also observed the superfluid transition of helium at 2.2K, without recognising its significance. The precise date and circumstances of the discovery were only reconstructed a century later, when Onnes' notebook was found. In subsequent decades, superconductivity was observed in several other materials. In 1913, lead was found to superconduct at 7K, and in 1941 niobium nitride was found to superconduct at 16K.

For the readers coming from a non-scientific background, in this section we will discuss temperature in terms of degrees Kelvin (K). Coldness in itself is not a distinct physical property. It is merely the lack of heat (energy) within a material. Once all of the energy possible has been removed, the material is said to be at absolute zero.

Absolute zero is the lower limit of the thermodynamic temperature scale, a state at which the enthalpy and entropy of a cooled ideal gas reaches its minimum value, taken as zero. Absolute zero is defined as precisely 0 K on the Kelvin scale, and it equates to -273.15 degrees Celsius on the Celsius scale with which we are all familiar.

In common with ferromagnetism and atomic spectral lines, superconductivity is a quantum mechanical phenomenon. The electrical resistivity of a metallic conductor decreases gradually as the temperature is lowered. In ordinary conductors such as copper or silver, this decrease is limited by impurities and other defects. Even near zero K, a normal conductor shows some resistance. In a superconductor, the resistance drops abruptly to zero when the material is cooled below its critical temperature. An electric current flowing through a loop of superconducting wire can persist indefinitely with no power source.

In 1986, it was discovered that some cuprate-perovskite ceramic materials have a critical temperature above 90K (-183°C). Such a high transition temperature is theoretically impossible for a conventional superconductor, leading to these new materials being termed as Class II or high temperature superconductors. Liquid nitrogen boils at 77 K, and superconduction at higher temperatures than this facilitated many experiments and applications that are less practical at lower temperatures.

The microscopic structure of high temperature superconductors has long puzzled scientists seeking to harness their virtually limitless technological potential. Now, at last, researchers have deciphered the cryptic structure of one class of the superconductors, providing a basis for theories about how they manage to transport electricity with perfect efficiency when cooled, and how scientists might raise their operating temperature closer to the climes of everyday life.

This goal, if realised, could make an array of fantastical technologies commercially viable, from power grids that never lose energy and cheap water purification systems to magnetically levitating vehicles. Scientists believe room-temperature superconductivity would have an impact on a par with that of the laser, a 1960s invention that now plays an important role in an estimated $7.5 trillion of economic activity.

Louis Taillefer, a professor of physics at the University of Sherbrooke in Quebec, has said, "In the same way that a laser is a lot more powerful than a light bulb, room temperature superconductivity would completely change how you transport electricity and enable new ways of using electricity."

Materials that superconduct under much warmer conditions than their ultra-cooled predecessors were discovered in 1986, winning IBM researchers Georg Bednorz and K. Alex Müller the Nobel Prize in Physics soon after. But today, around three decades later, our current high-temperature superconductors still fall short of room-temperature operation by more than 100°C. The materials' complexity has so far frustrated the dream of purpose-formulating their operating temperatures. Researchers currently say that new developments are firmly setting them on the right track.

Until 1986, scientists generally believed that the accepted knowledge of physics at the time forbade superconductivity at temperatures above around 30K. In that year, Bednorz and Müller discovered superconductivity in a lanthanum-based cuprate perovskite material, which had a transition temperature of 35 K, and as a result of this were awarded the Nobel Prize for Physics in 1987. It was soon found that replacing the lanthanum with yttrium raised the critical temperature to 92 K.

The primary superconducting components used by the author in the final, most powerful, version of his superconducting turbine (to be discussed in the next chapter) were constructed using yttrium barium cuprate (YBaCuO).

Since that time, other superconductors have been developed with even higher transition temperatures, but yttrium barium cuprate will superconduct above the boiling point of liquid nitrogen. This is an inexpensive and readily available industrial material, and lends itself well to research into Class II Superconductors.

Many other cuprate superconductors have since been discovered, and the theory of superconductivity in these materials is one of the major outstanding challenges of theoretical condensed matter physics. There are currently two main hypotheses – the resonating-valence-bond theory, and spin fluctuation, which has the most support in the research community. The second hypothesis proposed that electron pairing in high-temperature superconductors is mediated by short-range spin waves known as paramagnons.

Since 1993, the highest temperature superconductor was a ceramic material consisting of mercury, barium, calcium, copper and oxygen ($HgBa_2Ca_2Cu_3O_{8+\delta}$) with T_c = 133–138 K. The latter experiment (138 K) still awaits experimental confirmation, however.

In February 2008, an iron-based family of high-temperature superconductors was discovered. Hideo Hosono, of the Tokyo Institute of Technology, and colleagues found lanthanum oxygen fluorine iron arsenide ($LaO_{1-x}F_xFeAs$), an oxypnictide that superconducts below 26 K. Replacing the lanthanum in $LaO_{1-x}F_xFeAs$ with samarium leads to superconductors that work at 55 K.

Subir Sachdev, a professor of physics at Harvard University, recently predicted the form of charge density waves, which he detailed as a possible mechanism behind high-temperature superconductivity. Although further tests are needed, Sachdev's theory is gaining support from many experts, who say it succinctly captures key features of these materials. The various recent findings are at last starting to build a comprehensive picture of the physics behind high-temperature superconductivity.

High-temperature superconductivity seems like a miracle of quantum mechanics; one that could be harnessed to great effect if only it could be properly understood.

The property is exhibited primarily by cuprates, brittle ceramic materials composed of two-dimensional sheets of copper and oxygen separated by more complicated layers of atoms. When cuprates are cooled below a certain temperature, electrons in the copper-oxygen sheets suddenly overcome their mutual repulsion and pair up.

With their powers combined, they behave like a different type of particle altogether, a boson, which has the unique ability to join with other bosons into a coherent swarm that moves as one. This bosonic swarm perfectly conducts electricity. A current flowing through a loop of cuprate wire will persist forever, or as long as the liquid nitrogen fridge stays on. Taillefer correctly said that the biggest question in this field is what force binds the electrons together, because if you can understand that force, you can then strengthen the force.

In Class I superconductivity, the kind exhibited by many metals when they are cooled to near absolute zero, electron pairing is caused by gentle pressure waves that breeze through the metals. When an electron gets swept along by one of these waves, another follows in its wake, attracted by the positively charged metal atoms that shift toward the passing electron. But this light breeze cannot possibly explain pairing in cuprates, which survives at up to 160 K (-113 °C).

Many competing forces seem to influence the electrons simultaneously, and the force that binds them together over such a broad temperature range must be strong enough to overcome others that strive to keep them apart. The devil is in disentangling the forces. In the words of Pegor Aynailian, an assistant professor of physics at Binghamton University in New York, "It feels like we're in a battlefield and we don't know who's our ally and who's our enemy."

The first sign of what looks increasingly like the enemy – charge density waves, also known as "charge order" – came in 2002. Using a new kind of microscope that could map currents on the surface of cuprates with nanometer resolution, Davis, then a professor at the University of California, Berkeley, and Jennifer Hoffman, his graduate student at the time, discovered a minute pattern of denser and less-dense ripples of electrons.

These appeared wherever they hit the cuprate with a powerful magnetic field, an effect that suppressed superconductivity. Soon, other labs reported more actions that both killed superconductivity and produced the waves, such as raising the temperature or lowering the cuprates' oxygen concentration.

"You start to build this picture in which charge density waves are lurking, waiting to take over when anything unfriendly to superconductivity happens," said Hoffman, who is now an associate professor at Harvard.

It seemed possible that if the force shaping electrons into charge density waves could be suppressed, its rival, the force that forms superconducting pairs, would flourish. But some researchers argued that the ripples of electrons were merely a surface anomaly and irrelevant to superconductivity.

The community still remains divided today, when two groups using a technique called resonant X-ray scattering managed to detect charge density waves deep inside cuprates, cementing the importance of the waves. As the groups published their findings in *Science and Nature Physics*, two new collaborations formed, one led by Damascelli and the other by Ali Yazdani of Princeton University, with plans to characterise the waves even more thoroughly. Finishing in a dead heat, the rival groups' independent studies appeared together in *Science* in January 2014. They confirmed that charge density waves are a ubiquitous phenomenon in cuprates and that they strenuously oppose superconductivity, prevailing as the temperature rises.

CHAPTER 15

When I attended high school in the 1960s I was fascinated by many of the science experiments that we performed. One of the most intriguing to me was that you could make a metallic/dielectric sandwich apparently lose weight merely by applying a high-voltage differential between the two metal plates. How could this be? This apparent weight loss had occurred even though the sandwich assembly still had the same mass and was still under the same gravitation attraction as it was prior to the plates being charged. This and similar events prompted me to investigate these types of phenomena further when I was older and had more money and time available to do so.

We will now discuss a project to which I have devoted many years — the design and construction of a superconducting turbine that can generate a local gravitational field.

In physics, the graviton is a hypothetical elementary particle that mediates the force of gravitation in the framework of quantum field theory. If it exists, the graviton must be massless (because the gravitational force has unlimited range), and must have a spin of 2. This is because the source of gravitation is the stress-energy tensor, a second-rank tensor, compared to electromagnetism, the source of which is the force-current, a first-rank tensor. Additionally, it can be shown that any massless spin-2 field would be indistinguishable from gravitation, because a massless spin-2 field must couple to (interact with) the stress-energy tensor in the same way that the gravitational field does. The author believes that this spin-2 field is created inside the superconducting vortex generated by the turbine.

When the superconducting turbine is operating, and positrons interact with the zero-resistance electrons along the crystal boundaries, large forces are produced that drive the turbine.

The basic principle of operation of the superconducting turbine is to create a superconducting vortex. When you also have matter-antimatter annihilations taking place within this vortex, some quite exotic physics occurs.

I should state at this point that I was not the first person to investigate the properties of rotating superconductors, or to patent the equipment developed in order to protect the results achieved. I was fascinated by this whole area, as it really is cutting-edge physics, and you do not need the budget of CERN in order to investigate it.

I started by researching the work of all of the people who had gone before, and then purchased English translations of all of the patents that had been awarded in this field. After carefully studying these patents, I tried to think outside the box into reasons why other designers only managed to produce marginal and fairly weak artificial gravitational fields. I think that what they achieved was amazing in itself, but the results had little commercial value, as you can get a similar small reduction in gravity just by climbing up a mountain.

All of the prior work involved rotating superconducting discs at very high speeds, forcing the zero-resistance electrons within the superconductor to take curved paths. Unfortunately there is a limit to how fast you can rotate any mechanical assembly before it finally disintegrates.

I decided to remove this limitation by incorporating a counter-rotating electromagnetic field surrounding the spinning superconductor itself. This resulted in the zero-resistance electrons behaving as if the superconducting disc was spinning at an enormous speed, and increased the previously observed effects substantially. The counter-rotating field was initially rotated with a clock frequency of 1 Megahertz. This is equivalent to 60,000,000 rpm, and no mechanical assembly could possibly even get close to this level of rotational velocity.

This enabled me to reproduce the results demonstrated by others, but also to greatly increase the strength of the local gravitational field generated due to my innovation of including this counter-rotating field. This was recognised by the various international patent authorities to be an "inventive step", which is necessary in order to obtain a new patent which incorporates some features from earlier existing patents.

The second innovation, which was also considered an inventive step, was to incorporate the matter-antimatter annihilations within the vortex itself.

I consider myself to be very fortunate, as at the time I started developing the turbine, I was the CEO of a successful company in Aberdeen. The best thing about being a CEO is that provided you meet the profit targets that the board sets each year, you can pretty much do what you want. Most of them just play golf. The downside is that if you do not hit your targets you will be out of a job fairly rapidly, irrespective of how hard you have been working. My strategy in this area was to surround myself with a team of very competent staff. We all have strengths in certain areas, but are not so competent in other areas.

I believe that in order to be successful you must build a team of people who collectively will be very effective in every area that the business needs to operate. This includes technical, engineering, marketing, legal, health and safety and others. I employed a team of people to enable us to reach this goal, and achieve the requirements set by the board for the annual growth in company profits.

Once you have done this, you can generate a lot of free time to follow your own interests. I used to arrive at work very early each day, and check what had arrived from our overseas operations overnight. Sometimes certain technical tasks or the need to attend meetings cropped up, which I had to deal with myself. Other than these, I delegated the other tasks to the staff members best qualified to deal with each particular issue. I often finished my work by lunchtime, and then disappeared off to my private lab for the rest of the afternoon. My secretary was instructed to tell callers that I was in meetings unless it was an extremely serious situation.

The main business area of my company (NSI) was to develop innovative technical solutions to new challenges as they arose in the oil and gas industry worldwide. In order to perform this work, we were authorised by the Scottish EPA to hold quantities of many different radioactive isotopes, reactive chemicals, liquid nitrogen and other materials. As well as being the CEO, I was also the head of R&D. This ensured that in addition to being free to grow the company in a direction that would achieve the required financial growth, I also had access to virtually any materials and outsourced precision machining services etc. that I required for my own pet projects.

Before going into the details of the design concepts and operational principles of the superconducting turbine, I am starting this section with information regarding the first public demonstration of the equipment. The post-demonstration interview and draft PR release is now shown, followed by scans (Figures A and B) of the heavily sanitised version that was actually published following the demonstration.

Proposed press release:

ALTERNATIVE ENERGY – THE SUPERCONDUCTING TURBINE

Aberdeen geophysicist and entrepreneur Mike Bennett has now released details of a recently developed superconducting turbine. It is believed to have the potential to usher in a new chapter in energy efficient transportation.

The turbine uses axial superconductors to produce exceptionally high thrust to weight ratios. This equipment has so far shown the ability to accelerate any object or material at rates of up to 1.8 G, around 18 m/s/s. The turbine was recently demonstrated on objects of various sizes, shapes and construction materials, and the following interview was then conducted.

How does the turbine work?
Well basically, I am using class II superconductors coated with positron emitters and charged to many thousands of volts to produce a vortex with extremely high flux densities. By spinning both the source and drive fields at high speeds, a propulsive force is produced. This is known as a spin-2 field.

This equipment was built on a small budget, mostly from components salvaged from ex-medical and military equipment. Although it works well, it could be far more efficient if certain parts could be custom manufactured for the specific purpose for which they are now used.

How does this spin-2 field differ from a normal electromagnetic field?
An electromagnetic field will only act on certain materials, such as magnetic and diamagnetic substances. A spin-2 field will act on any material, and will apply the same acceleration to any object. I have tested it on metals, plastics, wood, many liquids and various other everyday objects.

The demonstration of the equipment then followed. After charging up the equipment, three objects – a large bolt, a length of wood and a bottle of soft drink – were placed above the turbine. The turbine was then run up to speed. At this point, the air surrounding the turbine ionised and emitted a blue/white light. All three objects then accelerated vertically and hit the ceiling.

What do you see as the potential uses for this turbine?
I think that the primary application will be in the field of transportation. When fully developed, the cost will probably be too high for cars and other surface transport, but the application to the aviation industry could be very significant.

How so?
I believe that if fitted to aircraft, fuel savings of up to

fifty percent could be achieved when compared to the fuel consumption of conventional turbine engines. A fifty percent reduction in fuel consumption would, for example, save British Airways alone over £1 billion annually on their fuel bills, in addition to the environmental benefits of avoiding the need to burn some three million tonnes of jet fuel. The commercial attraction of a superconducting turbine is therefore clear.

What is your educational background and experience in this field?

I graduated from the University of Manchester in 1979 with joint honours degrees in physics and geology. After five years working in the oil industry I founded my first company in 1984. This company adapted new technologies to help solve reservoir engineering problems and therefore maximise oil and gas recovery. We applied techniques and equipment normally only used by research physicists, and used them to solve problems in the real world. After building up the company over twelve years, I sold it on in 1996. I now work part-time as a consultant, in order to have more time to pursue my other interests.

What other new technologies have you successfully developed?

Initially, we built laser diffraction equipment to improve the completion quality of wells in the UK and Norwegian sectors of the North Sea. It took a while to obtain ABS and DNV certification for this equipment, but once in use offshore it proved to be very successful. In the 1990s, I visited the Brookhaven National Laboratory on Long Island to share the developments we had made in the North Sea. In return, I was briefed about techniques that they had developed for the US government for use on non-oil related projects. This research was then seeded back to the North Sea, and the new reservoir engineering techniques that we then pioneered on the UKCS are now industry standards worldwide.

Would you describe your talents as just being able to think outside the conventional box?
Well, not really. I have developed and patented equipment that is unique, but most of the commercial success has come from taking existing ideas and techniques that were developed in unrelated spheres, and developing them for a completely different use.

Finally, why are you making your current project public at this stage?
This technology is now ready for commercial development. However to develop and produce a final product requires financial resources that are beyond my means. I am therefore hoping to raise venture capital to enable this goal to be achieved.

CHAPTER 16

Following the demonstration of the superconducting turbine to industrialists in Aberdeen, I needed to expose this work to a wider audience. One of my good friends in Aberdeen is a gentleman called Alan Scott. He is an extremely colourful character, but a very intelligent and well-connected man. He was born and brought up in Ulster, and was an officer in the Royal Ulster Constabulary before he worked his way up in the publishing business to eventually become the managing director for DC Thompson Publishing in Scotland.

Every year DC Thompson would arrange an outing to the Perth Races for friends and associates. After an early breakfast in the pub, our group would be picked up by coach and driven down to the Perth Races. On the way, everyone was plied with champagne to the point where we were all extremely happy before we arrived.

I remember that after we had all boarded the coach, Alan would introduce everybody. The coach was full of dignitaries and major business players from the north-east of Scotland. The guests usually included the Lord Provost of Aberdeen, the Brigadier General in Command of the Gordon Highlanders Regiment, various knights of the realm, lords, and the list goes on. When Alan got to me I was merely introduced as English Mike.

We all know what corporate entertainment is like. By the end of the day in the coach on the way back home, we had all of these dignitaries singing *Tie Me Kangaroo Down, Sport*, *The Irish Rover* and *The Green Alligator Song*. We all had a really good day out. It is amazing how normal some of these upper-crust individuals can behave after you get to know them.

Alan's news group also had an executive box at Old Trafford. Every time there was a major match such as Manchester United playing in the Champions League at home, we would all fly down to Manchester for the day. It was yet more normal corporate entertainment, and after the first half you needed to close one eye or you would see two balls on the pitch.

Sometimes our corporate entertainment would take us abroad. On one occasion we had a golfing trip to the Spanish Costa Del Sol for a long weekend. Many senior dignitaries were on this trip, but they will not be named as they are whiter than white and squeaky clean when in the public spotlight. However, on this trip, there were two gentlemen in our group who were so inebriated the entire time that they never even managed to play golf at all.

We needed to rub their golf shoes over the grass and put some spare score cards in their luggage before they returned home, so that their families believed that they had in fact been on a golf tour.

The main newspaper that Alan presided over was the *Aberdeen Press and Journal*, although his company also printed the *News of the World* and other major newspapers for distribution within Scotland. The *P&J* is read throughout the UK, and I thought this was probably the best way forward for me to achieve the maximum free publicity.

Alan was always to be found in a certain bar in Aberdeen at lunchtime every Saturday. One Saturday I met up with him, and gave him the draft press release that had been prepared by my PR agent following the turbine demonstration. After plying him with a few single malts, he agreed that it would be the lead feature in his business section the following Thursday. However, soon after this article was published, I had my first face-to-face encounter with the security services.

I will now describe aspects of the security services that I have encountered during my career, particularly following the early demonstration of the superconducting turbine. I had to be very guarded in what I included in this section in order to get the book published.

I had my first confirmation that the security services are always operating behind the scenes, whether we know it or not, when I was living in Aberdeen. I had a sports fishing boat that I kept at Peterhead Marina to the north of

Aberdeen. It was an American boat, and I chose it because the dimensions were 25 feet long and 8.5 feet wide, which is just within the legal towing limits for an SUV on UK roads.

Peterhead is the biggest white fish port in the UK. It is also a major support base for the North Sea oil and gas industry. It is therefore very busy with commercial traffic. Before you are allowed to enter or leave the port you must obtain permission from the harbour master on VHF channel 14. This is sometimes quite difficult, as although you may have a very strong signal, their accents in this part of the north-east are so strong that they are often difficult to understand. I sometimes had to ask them to repeat the instructions, saying that the signal was breaking up.

One day when the children and I were boarding the boat for a fishing trip, I noticed dog paw marks on the decks. I thought this was strange because the marina is well-guarded and you need a key to gain entry through the high metal gates. On opening the cabin, I discovered that there were dog footprints inside there as well.

I contacted the marina manager, who informed me that the Grampian Police Special Forces were at the marina earlier in the week, and their dogs searched a number of boats for drugs and explosives. If it had not been for the fact that the dogs had wet paws, I would never have known this.

Anyway, we proceeded with our fishing trip. To the north of Peterhead there are very good fishing areas. The main pipelines carrying North Sea oil production are routed to St. Fergus, which is nearby. You can pick up the pipelines on sonar, and as the oil is still warm at this point there are normally a lot of fish around. We had a good day's fishing, but on the way back we were approached at speed by a large, orange, rigid inflatable boat carrying four men in black wetsuits. I assumed that they were a bunch of divers horsing about, so when they came very close to my boat I made a sharp turn and covered them all with spray.

They then produced a megaphone and informed me that they were Customs and Excise officers and they intended to board my vessel. During the day we had been over the horizon and therefore beyond the range of land-based radar, which is why I believe they intercepted us. They searched the boat from bow to stern, and even gutted three of the fish that we had caught to check what was inside them.

The remainder of this chapter deals with information that I have received from well-connected friends in the intelligence community. As it concerns the activities of the CIA, the NSA, British intelligence and Mossad, the names of some of the people involved have been changed.

While writing this chapter, the memories of Julian Assange come to mind. As I am sure the reader will recall, he was the founder of Wikileaks. He started the website when he decided that the activities of the American intelligence services had gone way beyond their remit. He therefore exposed information pertaining to this to the world in general.

Soon after this, when the Americans were unable to extradite him from the UK, somebody probably coerced the woman in Sweden to claim that he had sexually assaulted her. Under UK law, this was grounds for extradition. He knew that if he was extradited to Sweden he would end up in the US shortly thereafter, and they would probably lock him up and throw away the key.

At the time of writing he is still holed up in the Ecuadorian Embassy in London, knowing that if he steps outside he will be arrested by the British police and extradited.

Edward Snowden, who was a former intelligence analyst for the American secret service, is also in a similar position. He revealed details of their unauthorised covert surveillance of the American public, which also went far beyond their remit.

While I was working in the Middle East, my colleagues and I often went to Dubai at the weekends in order to get a drink and relax. There are a lot of other expats to be found in Dubai at the weekend for similar reasons. One evening we were talking to a couple of English guys who were in the same place as us. As the conversation progressed, I told them that I was based in Aberdeen, Scotland. I asked them if they had ever been to Scotland. They replied that they had both only been there once, and had stayed in Arbroath for two years. You then immediately know that they were with 45 Commando of the Royal Marines without them needing to tell you. No Englishman would go to Scotland once and stay in Arbroath for so long for any other reason.

When I told them this, they admitted that they were indeed ex-45 Commando, and were now working for a private security firm protecting people in Iraq. Although they never said so, I assumed that they were working for the main private security firm operating in the Middle East. I still keep in touch with them. I have since been told that following the Arab Spring uprising several years ago their company has created an independent commando unit of almost 1,000 troops based in Dubai. They consist mostly of mercenaries from South Africa and South America. This is because the UAE feel that should serious unrest arise within their own country, the local security services may not be willing to fire on fellow Muslims.

Let us now look at a CIA operation in the UK before we start to discuss the activities of Mossad. I was in Aberdeen at the time of the bombing of the Pan Am 747 over Lockerbie. I watched the whole thing unfold on TV and it was quite horrific. I was subsequently informed by a friend of mine who works in the Scottish police force that within hours of the crash, the Americans (presumably the CIA) were on the scene. He said that they took control of the initial stages of the investigation and recovery from the Scottish police force. I find this incredible, as they were reported to have been bagging and removing certain items from the crash scene.

It was later reported that e-mails had been sent from the US State Department to the US embassy and consulates in Germany advising that their personnel and their families returning home just before Christmas should not use this flight. The only explanation that I can think of for this is that either they knew something would happen to the aircraft, or they knew that something was on board that should not have been there.

Before I sold my first company I spent a lot of time in the Middle East, as a large proportion of our business came from this area. During that time, I was attempting to obtain new contracts in Iraq. This was immediately following Operation Desert Storm, and almost every part of their infrastructure needed to be rebuilt. I attempted to get contracts from many angles, but was always told that I must speak to a major US corporation operating in the region, which is widely believed to be the main overseas operating arm of the CIA. Although my company had been operating successfully in the Middle East for many years, we were unable to even get on the tender list for a single contract in Iraq.

A few years later, when I was back in Dubai again, I uncovered the reason for this. When in Dubai I usually stay with a friend who lives in the five-star Al Murooj Rotana complex just across the road from the Burj Khalifa tower, which was under construction at the time. While drinking in one of the bars in the complex one evening, I got talking to an American who was an extremely interesting gentleman. We got on well so he invited me up to his apartment for a party later that week. I saw a box of his business cards during the evening, and asked if it was okay to take one so I could contact him the next time I was in Dubai.

I then got one of my friends with the necessary security clearance to obtain information on him. He was indeed a US Navy Commander, as stated on his business card. However, I was informed that he worked at an Air Force Base in the desert nearby. I saw him leave the hotel one morning, picked up in a Humvee by men dressed in desert camouflage. I am almost certain that he must have been an important figure in US military intelligence. He did not live on the base but in a penthouse suite in a five-star hotel in Dubai. I have since been told that as he agreed to give me a business card and disclosed no information to me, I am permitted to name him as Commander B. Trout of the US Navy.

I subsequently spoke to another man from his base who I cannot name due to the information that he disclosed to me. I told him about the problems I was having even getting on the bid lists. He informed me that the company concerned was indeed the main commercial operating arm of the CIA, and the way it worked was as follows.

Before the Gulf War even started, the American military had precisely planned the key elements of the Iraqi infrastructure that were to be destroyed. He informed me that this company had already awarded the contracts for rebuilding all of the Iraqi infrastructure before the first bomb was even dropped. He told me that if you are not a US company, don't even bother to try to get the work. I should have suspected this, as during my many attempts to contact them I was often referred to an Admiral Cash (US Navy retired). He never did return my calls.

Now let us move on to Mossad. My knowledge of their activities stems from information that I was given by an Israeli friend who I've known for over twenty years. For the purposes of the book, I will call him Yuri. I trust him, as we have both helped each other on many occasions regarding business contacts etc.

As usual, my friends with good security clearances looked into him. Mossad is very secretive, which is probably why they are so effective. The most I could find out was that he was listed as a Colonel in the Israeli army, but I am almost certain that he is a former Mossad operative due to the incredible detail that he told me about some of their operations. He never admitted to this, and said that the information came from a military liaison officer who had contacts inside Mossad. Whatever.

One of the most fascinating operations that he revealed to me was the detail of the Israeli strike on Saddam Hussein's nuclear reactor. At the height of his power, Saddam Hussein decided that Iraq needed a nuclear reactor for peaceful energy generation. Nobody was quite sure why he needed this, as Iraq pretty much floats on oil.

Obligingly, the French, who are notorious for selling just about anything to anybody so long as they can make a buck, agreed to build one for him. Yuri told me that Mossad agents were quietly laughing among themselves, as they knew more about what was going on than the Iraqis themselves.

I think that Mossad may well have been in cahoots with the French on this one. They waited until the construction of the reactor was completed, and the French received their final staged payment. Following the completion of the reactor, and before the fuel was actually shipped from France, the Israelis decided to take it out.

They sent in a squadron of F-15s to do the job, but they needed to fly through Saudi airspace. They therefore put an Arabic-speaking interpreter into one of the warplanes. As they entered Saudi airspace they were confronted by the Saudi ground controllers. The Israelis told them that they were a military training flight, and the inept Saudi controllers fell for it.

The attack was timed so that they would approach the reactor at dawn out of the rising sun. The first wave of aircraft demolished the protective concrete dome over the reactor, and the second wave completely destroyed the reactor itself. All of the aircraft returned safely to Israel.

Everybody knows about the raid on Entebbe due to the books and films that have been produced on the subject.

However, another episode that Yuri related to me that I did not know about was further details of the Iraqi supergun story.

When in power, Saddam Hussein realised that he had no chance of penetrating Israeli airspace with warplanes, so he bought scud missiles from the Russians. The Israelis had a good deal of success in intercepting them, so he decided to build the world's largest gun so he could shell Tel Aviv from within Iraq. The gun was supposed to have a calibre of around one metre, and be capable of firing shells weighing several tons.

At the time, there were only two companies in the world capable of building a gun barrel of this size. The contract was given to Forge Masters in Sheffield, and the construction of the barrel began. Due to its size, it had to be constructed from many sections, which would be joined together once the gun was on location. The order was allegedly for pipeline parts for the Iraqi petroleum industry, but the technical specification was so tight that people within the company started to question what the actual purpose of this heavy-duty pipe really was.

The man who designed the gun turned out to be Dr Gerald Bull, who was the lead engineer of the HARP (High Altitude Research Project) team, and probably one of the world's foremost experts in the design of long-distance artillery. When Mossad got wind of the project, Dr Bull was quietly murdered one evening, and the British Customs were alerted to the real purpose of these pipes.

They were promptly impounded before leaving England, and Saddam Hussein never got his supergun.

I believe that this type of thing goes on all the time. I believe that it also happens in the UK if you are perceived to be a serious risk to upsetting the status quo. Although I have no independent knowledge other than what has been reported in the press, I remember the case of the hapless scientist who had been summoned to be an expert witness on weapons of mass destruction at a parliamentary hearing.

Although he had done nothing at all wrong himself, and had no history of any type of mental illness, we were told that he committed suicide just days before the hearing. His only mistake was to advise the government on WMD, the evidence of which was used as the basis for Britain going to war, and then be required to reveal what he actually told them under oath.

My initial direct encounter with the Secret Services themselves came soon after the superconducting turbine became operational. One afternoon I was visited by two men and a woman. The men were dressed in dark suits, and the woman was wearing an expensive-looking business jacket and skirt. I initially thought that they were Mormons or some other sect canvassing for money. However, without showing any identification, they started to question me about the turbine. I told them that without identification, I was not prepared to speak to them and they should leave.

How could they know about this? I was so concerned that after they left, I removed and hid the key components from the turbine under the insulation in the roof. Within hours, uniformed officers from the Grampian police force entered my premises with a warrant. The entire turbine (they thought) complete with all of the ancillary control equipment was confiscated. I was informed that my activities were in breach of radio communications legislation, and that the equipment was allegedly causing serious disruption to important communication networks in the area.

The next day I distributed the key components of the turbine to my friends around Aberdeen. I suspected that when their experts examined it, they would discover that key pieces were missing and return.

As already discussed, prior to designing the super-conducting turbine, I examined the other patents that had been awarded in this area to establish the current state of the art in this technology. The most significant work that I found was a German patent awarded eight years previously (DE 198 32 001 A1). I then tried to think outside of the conventional box in order to develop this basic concept. The inventive steps that I incorporated were accepted by the international patents authorities, allowing me to proceed with my own patent application.

In the next chapter I include the full description, operating principles and drawings of the superconducting turbine as they were originally filed with the patent office (UK

IPO). I have been informed that this is acceptable, as this information was already in the public domain prior to my first direct encounter with the security services.

CHAPTER 17

The original patent with a detailed description and drawings are now shown. The documents and technical drawings pertaining to this patent are shown in Figures C to H.

DEVICE FOR MOVING A MASS AND/OR GENERATING A FORCE EFFECTIVE FOR MODIFYING THE GRAVITATIONAL FIELD BETWEEN MASSES AND A METHOD THEREOF

The present invention relates to a device for moving a mass and/or generating a force effective for modifying the gravitational field, and in particular to a turbine adapted to generate a propulsive force or thrust, induced by interaction of strong coupling between electromagnetism and gravitation and electron-positron annihilation in a superconductor exposed to a rotating electromagnetic field. Furthermore, the present invention relates to a method for generating such a force.

INTRODUCTION

Gravitation, or gravity, is a natural phenomenon by which physical bodies attract each other with a force proportional to the mass and the reciprocal of the distance between the two bodies. A typical example of the effect of gravity is an object with a mass falling to the surface of the Earth when dropped from a height above that surface. Gravitation is also responsible for keeping planets or satellites in orbit around a larger mass. For example, planets of our solar system orbit around the sun and the moon orbits around the Earth due to the gravitational effects between these masses.

Furthermore, gravitation is one of the four fundamental interactions of nature, along with electromagnetism and the strong and weak interaction. In modern physics, gravitation is described using the general theory of relativity in which gravitation is a consequence of the curvature of space-time, which governs the motion of inertial objects. Thus, in the framework of quantum field theory, it is possible to describe gravity analogue to the other fundamental forces, such that the attractive force of gravity arises due to exchange of virtual gravitons, in the same way as the electromagnetic force arises from exchange of virtual photons. That said, this approach fails at short distances of the order of the Planck length (1.616252×10-35 meter), where a more complete theory of quantum gravity is required. However, the simpler Newton's law of universal gravitation provides an accurate approximation for most calculations.

Therefore, it is generally understood that when moving any object with a mass in a direction other than towards the direction of the gravitational field (i.e. the gravitational field of the Earth), a force has to act on the object to overcome the effects of that gravitational field.

For example, in order to move an aeroplane up and through the air, sufficient force has to be generated by its engine(s) to overcome the Earth's gravitational field. The required force is provided by aerodynamic lift generated from the aeroplane's wings moving through the air at a speed above a predetermined threshold. The required speed may be provided by thrust that is generated by the aeroplane's jet engines. Jet engines are, simply put, internal combustion engines powered by a turbine in which fuel combustion is used to generate mechanical energy. From this example, it is clear that overcoming the Earth's gravitational field is one of the major factors responsible for the engine's fuel efficiency. Thus any means that could either shield or modify the effects of the Earth's gravitational field would have a considerable effect on the fuel consumption of any engine utilized to oppose gravity and may therefore significantly decrease the costs of transportation.

In the currently available state of the art, various aspects of gravity control have been hypothesized, theorized, tested and examined by numerous research groups and individuals in order to find alternative means of propulsion.

For example, in the first half of the 20th century, Prof. Biefeld and T.T. Brown discovered that a high potential charged capacitor with dielectrics exhibited unidirectional thrust towards the positively charged plate when the atoms of a material are placed within the electric field of a capacitor. This phenomenon is called the *Biefeld-Brown* effect, which suggests a strong coupling between electricity and gravitation. Subsequently, the term *"electrogravitics"* has been widely used in connection with the *Biefeld-Brown* effect since the mid-20th century.

It is hypothesized that electrogravitic processes use an electric field to charge or, more properly, polarize an object and counteract the effects of gravity.

More recently, Bernard Haisch, Harold E. Puthoff, and several other physicists have shown connections between electromagnetism, notably the electromagnetic zero-point field, and inertia, and have speculated about possible further connections with gravity. Physicist Ning Li and engineer Eugene Podkletnov have, respectively, shown theoretically, and reported observing experimentally, anomalous gravitic attenuation effects above a superconducting disk spinning in a strong magnetic field, such as is produced in a *Meissner effect* demonstration apparatus. Giovanni Modanese has conducted further experiments on the phenomena seen by Podkletnov and has reported some additional, much stronger, but transient, anomalous gravitational effects.

However, according to the current state of the art, none of the above experiments or calculations were able to demonstrate a local decrease of the gravitational field that could practically be utilized for generating a propulsive force.

Accordingly, it is an object of the present invention to provide a propulsion engine or improve the efficiency of propulsion engines by modifying the gravitational field.

SUMMARY OF THE INVENTION

Preferred embodiments of the invention seek to overcome one or more of the above disadvantages of the prior art.

According to a first aspect of the present invention, there is provided a device for generating a force suitable for moving a mass and/or modifying the gravitational effect of masses, comprising:

- a layer assembly rotatable about said centre axis, comprising at least:
- a first dielectric layer arranged at one end of said layer assembly,
- a superconducting layer adapted to be electrically connected to a high voltage generator during use,
- a positron emitter layer adapted to emit positrons toward said superconducting layer, and
- a second dielectric layer arranged at the other end of said layer assembly,

wherein said device further comprises a plurality of diametrically opposed field plates adapted to provide an electromagnetic field within said layer assembly that is counter-rotating to said direction of rotation of said layer assembly.

Preferably, the layer assembly is axially symmetrical with respect to a centre axis, except for one or more electrodes which may be located at differing radii. Typically, the layer assembly is rotatable at a first predetermined rotational speed about said centre axis. Preferably, the positron layer is operatively mounted above said superconducting layer when in use. Preferably, the said electro-magnetic field is counter-rotating to said direction of said layer assembly at a second predetermined rotational speed.

Advantageously, the arrangement of the current invention allows the annihilation of accelerated superconducting electrons with β+ positrons in the boundary region of the crystal structured superconducting layer and the positron emitter, while the electron-positron annihilation is superimposed by an electromagnetic field, which is counter-rotating with respect to the rotation of the superconducting layer, therefore, generating a local gravitational field that either increases or decreases the Earth's gravitational field depending on its direction with respect to the Earth's gravitational field. Thus, the resultant force may advantageously be used as a separate propulsive force of a vehicle. On the other hand, the resultant force may be used in addition to a propulsive force generated by a common engine, such as a turbine, in order to considerably improve the fuel efficiency of that engine.

The second predetermined rotational speed may be greater than the first predetermined rotational speed.

The layer assembly may be mounted to a drive shaft operatively coupleable to a motor.

This allows the advantage that a standard motor can be used to rotate the layer assembly about its centre axis. In particular, the drive shaft may be coupled to the motor via a 90° bevel gear, further allowing the motor to be situated remote and off-axis from the rotation axis of the layer assembly, therefore avoiding possible obstruction of the propulsive force by the motor.

The device of the present invention may further comprise a thermally insulating housing adapted to receive at least the layer assembly and maintain layer assembly at or below the critical temperature Tc, at which the super-conductor becomes superconducting for a finite time period during use.

This provides the advantage that the conditions required to work a superconductor can be created relatively cost effectively. In particular, the superconductor is simply placed in the thermally insulating housing, which is cooled to the required temperature Tc by simply filling the housing with a coolant. Once the superconducting layer is cooled to the predetermined temperature Tc, the coolant may be removed before running the embodiment of the present invention.

The device may further comprise a controller adapted to sequentially generate an electromagnetic field between the plurality of diametrically opposed field plates.

This provides the advantage that very high switching speeds of the opposing plates can be reached, therefore resulting in a rotational speed of the electromagnetic field that is considerably faster than the rotational speed of the layer assembly.

The layer assembly may further comprise a first electrode and a second electrode, each arranged through the first dielectric layer and electrically connected to the superconducting layer and located at respective first distance and second distance relative to the centre axis.

The first electrode and the second electrode may be adapted to receive a voltage from a high voltage generator during use.

This provides the advantage that a fixed, predetermined voltage can be provided to the superconducting layer from any suitable external voltage generator that is not limited to a specific size and/or location.

The first distance may be greater than the second distance.

This provides the advantage that the zero-resistant electrons travelling from the first electrode to the second electrode within the rotating superconducting layer are forced onto a spiral path on which the speed of the electrons increases despite the constant angular velocity of the rotating disc. Thus, the electrons are accelerated on a path within the rotating superconducting layer before annihilation with the emitted positrons while exposed to a high-speed counter-rotating electromagnetic field. The interactions effective at the boundary region between the superconductor layer and the positron emitter are believed to allow strong electrogravitic coupling generating a local gravitational field capable of modifying the Earth's gravitational field.

The first electrode and the second electrode may be adapted to counterbalance each other during use.

This provides the advantage that the rotating layer assembly is sufficiently balanced to allow an undisturbed rotation about its centre axis.

The first electrode and the second electrode may be connectable to a high voltage generator via sliding contacts or frictionless electric arcs.

The first and second dielectric layer, the positron emitter layer and the superconducting layer may be of an annular disc shape.

According to a second aspect of the present invention there is provided a method for generating a force suitable for moving and/or modifying the gravitational effect of masses using a device according to the first aspect of the present invention, comprising the steps of:

(a) cooling the layer assembly to a predetermined temperature suitable for generating a superconducting effect in the superconducting layer of said layer assembly,

(b) providing a positron source adapted to emit positrons towards the superconducting layer of said layer assembly,

(c) rotating the layer assembly about a centre axis at a first predetermined rotational speed,

(d) alternately charging and discharging the superconducting layer using a high voltage generator at a frequency proportional to said first predetermined rotational speed,

(e) concurrently to step (d), generating a electromagnetic field within the layer assembly counter-rotating relative to the direction of rotation of the layer assembly at a second predetermined rotational speed.

Step (a) may be effected by operatively positioning the layer assembly in a thermally insulating housing and filling the thermally insulating housing with a coolant.

Step (b) may be effected by mounting the layer assembly to a drive shaft which is operatively coupled to a motor.

The counter-rotating electromagnetic field may be generated by a controller sequentially charging and discharging the diametrically opposed field plates with a predetermined voltage.

The second predetermined rotational speed may be greater than the first predetermined rotational speed.

BRIEF DESCRIPTION OF THE DRAWINGS

A preferred embodiment of the present invention will now be described, by way of example only and not in any limitative sense, with reference to the accompanying drawings, in which:

- Figure E shows a partial sectional side view along A-A of a preferred embodiment of the present invention,
- Figure F shows a sectional top view along B-B of the embodiment of Figure E,
- Figure G shows an exploded perspective view of all main components of the preferred embodiment and a simplified view of the main component's function,
- Figure H shows schematic plan view of the rotating superconducting layer and the predicted path of the electrons during operation, .

DETAILED DESCRIPTION OF EMBODIMENTS

Referring to Figures E, F and G, a preferred example of a turbine incorporating the present invention is disclosed comprising a device for generating a force effective for modifying the gravitational field between masses. The turbine further comprises a layer assembly 102 mounted onto a base plate 104 of a drive shaft 106, a motor 108 that is coupled to the drive shaft 106 via a 90° bevel gear mechanism 109 and a drive field system 110 having four pairs of diametrically opposed field plate pairs 112a, 112b, 112c, 112d powered and driven by a controller 114. The plates of the field plate pairs 112a, 112b, 112c, 112d may be made from metal and in particular from Copper. The base plate 104 is further in electrical connection to the drive shaft 106, both of which are earthed.

The controller 114, which includes a power supply (not shown), may also drive the external motor 108. It is understood that the invention is not limited to the 90° bevel gear mechanism 109 or an external motor 108, and any other suitable means for operatively coupling the drive shaft 106 to any suitable drive means may be used. Also, any other suitable means for rotating the layer assembly 102 about its central axis may be used.

As shown in Figures E and F, the layer assembly 102 comprises a first and second dielectric layer 118, 124, which form the top and bottom layers with respect to the bottom base plate 104 of drive shaft 106. A superconducting layer 120 and a positron emitter layer 122, deposited directly above the superconducting layer 120 with respect to the bottom base plate 104, form the centre section of the layer assembly 102. A first and second electrode 126, 128 pass through the second dielectric layer 124 and the adjacent positron emitter layer 122 to electrically connect the superconducting layer 120 to a high voltage generator 130. The electrical contact between the first and second electrode 126, 128 and the high voltage generator 130 may be made via sliding contacts (not shown). However, any other electrical contact means may be used, such as electric arc or plasma.

Referring now to Figure H, the first electrode 126 may be located concentrically with respect to the drive shaft 106 and its rotational axis at a radius R1 and the second electrode 128 may be located concentrically with respect to the drive shaft 106 and its rotational axis at a radius R2. Preferably, first and second electrode 126, 128 are positioned on a diameter of the layer assembly 102 opposed to drive shaft 106. In this particular example, radius R1 is greater than radius R2 such that the zero-resistant electrons e- that travel from the first electrode 126 to the second electrode 128 within the rotating superconducting layer 122 are forced onto a spiral path. First and second electrodes 126 and 128 are balanced in weight according to their distance from the rotational axis of the layer assembly 102.

Preferably, the superconducting layer 120 is made from an Yttrium Barium Cuprate compound, but any other suitable superconducting or high-temperature superconducting material may be used. Also, the positron emitter layer 122 may be a 22Na isotope which provides β+ positrons 121 according to the decay reaction 22Na → 22Ne + β+ + ve + γ. However, any other suitable positron source may be used. The first and second dielectric layer 118, 124 may be made from solid polycarbonate material or any other electrically insulating material.

The drive field system 110 and the layer assembly 102 are concentrically arranged within a thermally insulating housing 116 such that the layer mechanism 102 and the drive system 110 share the same rotational plane with respect to the rotational axis 107 of the drive shaft 106. The opening of the thermally insulating housing may be sealed by a lid 117 that fits between the housing interior walls and the drive shaft 106. The housing may further comprise an inlet port 132 and an outlet port 134 for introducing and removing a coolant 136, such as, for example, liquid nitrogen. In this particular example, the rotatable drive shaft 106 may be supported by twin bearings (not shown) positioned outside the thermally insulating housing 116.

An example of the operation of the preferred embodiment and the method for generating a force effective for modifying the gravitational field between masses is now described with reference to Figures E to H.

Prior to starting the turbine 10, liquid nitrogen 136 is introduced into the housing 116 through an inlet port 132 soaking the layer assembly 102 until its temperature is cooled to below the critical temperature Tc of the superconducting layer 120. Excessive liquid nitrogen 136 is then removed from the housing 116 through an outlet port 134 until the surface level of the liquid nitrogen 136 is below the base plate 104. The remaining coolant 136 is left within the housing 116 to maximize the time period until the temperature within the housing rises above Tc. The coolant 136 may also be introduced via the top opening of the housing 116 by removing and replacing the lid 117.

As soon as the critical temperature Tc of the superconducting layer 120 is reached, the motor 108 is started by the controller 114, thereby rotating the drive shaft 106 and layer assembly 102 at about 3,500 rpm. At the same time, the high voltage generator 130 charges and discharges the superconducting layer 120 via respective first and second electrodes 126 and 128 with each rotation of the layer assembly 102. The voltage used to charge the superconducting layer 120 in this particular example is in the region of 20,000 V DC. The positron emitter layer 122 deposited on the top surface of the superconducting layer 120 provides a constant supply of β+ positrons 121 that are directed towards the superconducting layer 120 in which electrons (e-) move at zero-resistance from the first electrode 126 to the second electrode 128 in response to the high voltage charge provided by the high voltage generator 130. When electrons e- and positrons 121 collide, both particles are annihilated creating gamma ray photons according to e- + β+ → γ + γ.

At the same time, the controller 114 sequentially switches a high voltage to each of the drive field plate pairs 112a, 112b, 112c and 112d producing an electromagnetic field 138 of high flux density rotating in the opposite direction to the rotation of the layer assembly 102. In particular, drive field plate pair 112a may be switched to a potential of -3,500 V DC / +3,500 V DC first, before the drive field plate pair 112a is switched off and the next drive field plate pair 112b is switched on to the same potential. The sequence continues with drive field plate pair 112c and drive field plate pair 112d, before it starts again with drive field plate pair 112a.

The controller 114 may use a switching array of high voltage Insulated Gate Bipolar Transistors (IGBT's) controlled by a 1 MHz clock speed to power and drive the plate pairs 112a, 112b, 112c, 112d, therefore, allowing a very high rotational field speed in the order of 250,000 x 60 rpm, i.e. 15,000,000 rpm, which, in this particular example, is 4,000 times faster than the used rotational speed of the layer assembly 102. Thus, the counter-rotating drive field 138 is rotating at a much higher speed than the layer assembly 102. It is understood that other suitable switching means may be used to drive the counter-rotating electromagnetic field 138 via drive field plate pairs 112a, 112b, 112c and 112d.

In this particular example, a propulsive force is generated in a direction normal to the rotational plane of the layer assembly 102 and the drive field 138. It is believed that the propulsive force is generated in response to a local gravitational field formed by electrogravitic coupling and the electron e- / positron 121 annihilation at the crystal boundaries where the superconducting layer 120 is in contact with the positron emitter layer 122.

The above described invention may also be applied to fields of technology other than transportation and the reduction of fuel consumption. For example the present invention may be used to create specific environment conditions on the Earth's surface that allow new drugs or vaccines to be studied and manufactured or new treatments to be developed. Furthermore, the present invention may allow the manufacture of semiconductors having ultra pure crystal matrices, or new alloys and composites with precisely controlled crystal boundaries.

It will be appreciated by persons skilled in the art that the above embodiment has been described by way of example only and not in any limitative sense, and that various alterations and modifications are possible without departing from the scope of the invention as defined by the appended claims.

– END OF PATENT DESCRIPTION –

Following the confiscation of my superconducting turbine, I was in a slight quandary about how to proceed. It was clear to me that the developments I had made on existing superconducting gravity work were very significant, and there was an enormous commercial application for this technology, but it was difficult to decide the best way forward.

Although my equipment had been confiscated by uniformed officers from the Grampian police force, the events over the coming weeks left me in no doubt that this confiscation was carried out at the behest of the Americans. The reason for this is that my military/industrial contacts in the US would no longer even return my calls.

The author Nick Cook had already informed me that I would be firmly on the radar of the NSA and other US security agencies after the development of my superconducting turbine was made public. How right he actually was.

I had previously held meetings and conducted business with many organisations within the United States, including their top research laboratories. In order to understand how American industrial and military research is performed, the reader needs to understand that there are two entirely different sides to their operations. Firstly you have organisations which perform work in the public eye, such as the NASA Jet Propulsion Laboratory in Pasadena, and many others. They oversee space exploration and many other technologies that are in the public view.

There is also a highly compartmentalised group of facilities that Nick Cook referred to as their black operations. A good deal of the research that is performed in support of the black operations is conducted at three major US national laboratories. These are the Los Alamos National Laboratory in New Mexico, the Oak Ridge National Laboratory in Tennessee and the Brookhaven National Laboratory in New York State.

Prior to the public disclosure regarding the development of my superconducting turbine, I would regularly contact these national laboratories. When I needed to purchase specialised nuclear materials, I had no problems in obtaining deliveries of these materials, as I operated a high-tech company that they could confirm as being a legitimate supplier of these materials to the oil and gas industry.

Before the details of my superconducting turbine were made public, I had visited the Brookhaven National Laboratory. The purpose of my initial meeting was to visit a scientist called Russ Dietz, who was a section head within one of their groups at the time. His group was interested in the developments that my company had made in the North Sea relating to laser diffraction particle analysis in completion fluids, which he thought would be of interest to his group.

Although this meeting was only scheduled for two hours, I spent the entire day talking with Russ and his group about our operations in the oil and gas industry. In return, he was very forthcoming in providing me with information that his group had previously researched for completely unrelated applications.

Prior to the Trinity test of the US atomic bomb, Brookhaven undertook groundwater studies in the test area to ensure that no contamination of aquifers supplying urban population centres would occur as a result of the nuclear test. For this purpose, they developed materials in the group of chemicals known as fluoro-benzoic acids. These materials can be detected at sub part per billion levels when derivatised and analysed using gas chromatography. This group at Brookhaven had developed a whole family of uniquely identifiable fluoro-benzoic acids for this purpose. I was given all of the research information that they had obtained. I subsequently used this research to develop new applications in water flood operations in the oil and gas industry. These materials have now become the worldwide standards in water tracing.

The first time that I was due to visit the Brookhaven National Laboratory, my wife, who was very good at reading my e-mails and other communications, got wind of the fact that I would be flying to New York the following week. She had never been there before, and wanted to come with me to do some shopping on Fifth Avenue. She certainly did not need any more clothes, and I figured that this holiday was just to impress her peer group. I informed her of the purpose of my trip, and that I would spend most of my time meeting with various scientists and engineers, but she insisted on accompanying me anyway.

We arrived in New York three days before my first scheduled meeting. We spent the time shopping and taking in the sights, and I'm sure she had a good time. On the day of my first meeting, my wife said that she would like to come with me as her credit cards (and mine) had already almost self-combusted by that time. I told her that I did not think that she would be allowed to attend, but I let her come anyway just to keep the peace.

Brookhaven National Laboratory is located on the southern coast of Long Island, close to New York City. We arrived first thing in the morning, and were initially stopped by the security personnel at the outer periphery of the site. We needed to show our passports at this point, and the security personnel then phoned through to the complex in order to confirm that we had been authorised to visit the facility. The security guards at Brookhaven look exactly like NYPD officers, except that their shoulder badges displayed the Brookhaven emblem. When the security guard returned, I was instructed to leave our car and to get into one of their own vehicles before proceeding into the facility.

My wife got out of the car at the same time, planning to come with me. The security officer said, "Ma'am, you are not on the approved visitors list, and without an invite you don't get into Brookhaven." My poor wife had to spend the next seven hours sitting alone in our hire car waiting for me to return.

In order to pursue my dream for the commercial development of my superconducting turbine, I thought that I would need to establish a facility outside of Europe and the USA. At that time, we already had a facility in an industrial complex in Mussafah, just outside Abu Dhabi. This seemed like an ideal location, as it had ready access to liquid nitrogen and many other industrial materials, together with precision machining services and everything else needed for the construction of another turbine.

My turbine operations were then transferred to Mussafah. At the time we had a very good agent there. If you need to conduct business in most of the countries in the Arab world, you need an agent. The agent obtains work permits for the personnel, licences for the import of the various materials required, and makes sure that you are in compliance with all of the local and national regulations. As all of the official paperwork must be filled out in Arabic, you need an agent to operate in these countries. The agents there charge you ten percent of the gross value of every invoice that you issue, but this is not a problem as you merely add this cost to your price list in order to recover the money. The agent is only paid after your invoices are paid, which provides him with the incentive to make sure that your invoices are paid promptly.

Construction of the next turbine then began. My initial turbine had a single-walled housing to contain the liquid nitrogen required to cool the superconducting assembly to below its critical temperature.

The main operational problem with this was that all of the liquid nitrogen needed to boil off prior to starting the turbine, as running the turbine in a liquid would not allow a sufficient rotational speed to be achieved. When the first turbine was operating, heat generated from the operation would cause the critical temperature of the superconductor assembly to be reached within about fifteen to twenty seconds, meaning that each operation was very limited in its duration.

The second turbine, developed in Abu Dhabi, was constructed using a double-walled turbine housing. This allowed the constant circulation of liquid nitrogen around the turbine space, in order to allow longer-duration testing to be performed. As a result of these and other developments, we produced a final design which was then prepared for commercial production.

About twelve months into the operation, we had a break-in at the facility, which was recorded on the discrete security cameras that we had installed. Although nothing was stolen, despite thousands of dollars' worth of equipment being located on the premises, the intruders merely photographed everything and then left. This left me in no doubt that this facility was attracting unwanted attention.

I then decided to move the operation to Jebel Ali. Jebel Ali is a free trade zone located between Abu Dhabi and Dubai. This zone has far better security, and you cannot enter the complex without authorisation. Operations continued at Jebel Ali until the final turbine design was completed and proven.

Within days of the project's completion, we were visited by the local police. For a second time, everything was confiscated, again on the grounds of alleged interference with radio communications systems. During the turbine development, I constantly measured and recorded the emissions from the turbine when it was operating. Although the turbine emits wide-spectrum electromagnetic radiation while operating, this was largely shielded by a special jacket installed around the turbine housing.

When very close to the turbine, the EM field would light any fluorescent tubes, and the turbine produced gamma ray dose rates in excess of 7.5 µSv per hour, making it a controlled area under the EU Ionising Radiation Regulations (IRR). However, outside the building itself, the gamma ray emission levels were negligible and mobile phone operation was not hindered.

There is no doubt in my mind that this excuse was used again and that the whole police operation was conducted at the behest of the US security services. As the UAE purchases most of their military equipment from the US, I guess that they must do what they are told if they want the latest ground attack radar to be installed in their F-18 warplanes.

Following this second equipment confiscation, which again caused me to shut down my operations, I was told by the authorities in no uncertain terms that if I ever pursued this project in the future, my feet would not touch the ground. I then remembered what my friend Yuri had told me about Dr Bull and the Iraqi supergun project, so I figured that I should heed their warning.

Some colleagues have since asked me why the authorities would want to shut this technology down. I believe that the answer is clear, as the United States is sitting on an absolute treasure trove of seized Nazi technology which includes gravity drive. It is not in their interest to reveal this information, although some of this technology is occasionally drip-fed to US industry.

The reason why it is not in the interest of the US is because giant American corporations such as Exxon Mobil, Conoco Phillips, Boeing and General Motors etc. employ millions of staff and generate hundreds of billions of dollars in tax revenue for the US economy. Any technology introduced that would negate the need for petroleum products as an energy source, or revolutionise the established transportation industry, would not be in the interests of their economy.

Some of this Nazi technology is occasionally released to benefit American corporations, probably due to their cooperation with the government in other areas. A good example of this is that when the Nazis were conducting their Russian campaign on the Eastern front, the winter temperatures were so cold that tank crews needed to light fires under the engine sumps every morning, as the viscosity of the oil had increased to the point where the engines would not turn over or start.

This problem was solved by German chemists, who produced the first ever fully synthetic oil, the viscosity of which would allow the tank engines to be started in the severe cold of the Russian winter. This technology was later released by Mobil Oil, as an ultra-high-performance lubricant which they claimed was the world's first fully synthetic motor oil, and they branded it "Mobil 1".

This was an almost direct copy of the Nazi tank engine oil, and it led to Mobil dominating the world market in engine oil for high-performance cars for decades. Not surprisingly, it is recommended by Porsche. Dr Ferdinand Porsche was an important business figure during the days of the Third Reich, and a close friend to Hitler. He was a brilliant engineer, and I have owned several of his 911 Carrera models, which are fantastic cars. However,when you trade in your current Porsche for a new model, the main thing that determines the trade-in price is the service record. If the car has not been serviced by an authorised dealer, and has not been refilled with Mobil 1 oil, you will lose a substantial amount of money on the residual value of the car.

Other examples of this technology release are suspected in some products launched by DuPont. During the 1940s, German chemists developed new fabric dyes that were previously unavailable. They could produce virtually the entire spectrum of vivid colours that were the envy of textile dye manufacturers the world over. It is suspected that after favours DuPont may have performed for the US government, they obtained the information on how to produce these materials.

I used to purchase tens of thousands of dollars' worth of specialised materials from the DuPont facility in Wilmington, Massachusetts. Although I paid all of their invoices promptly, and even purchased their entire world stock of a perfluorocarbon known as "Vertrel 245" (aka Perfluoro Di Methyl Cyclo Butane, or PDMCB) they are yet another major US corporation that will no longer sell me anything. No problem, as today I can purchase everything that I require from Russian suppliers.

DuPont also developed and patented the non-stick product that we all know as Teflon. Teflon is a temperature-resistant perfluorocarbon, but its application revolutionised the manufacture of kitchenware. The name Teflon is a DuPont copyright, however many other kitchenware manufacturers now use the same coating but are unable to use the word Teflon when describing the coating, although it is usually exactly the same material. Teflon is another perfluorocarbon thought to have been developed by Nazi scientists as a by-product of their research into producing artificial blood.

CHAPTER 18

It was a warm summer's morning in 2008, and I had just arrived by train at Paddington station in London. We were on our way to meet my father who had retired to live in Cornwall in south-west England. However that day I had a meeting with the investigative journalist and author Nick Cook.

When the children were younger, we often went down to visit my father. However the distance from north-east Scotland to south-west England required two separate flights, together with a one-hour car journey after you arrived at the nearest airport in Devon. Because of this, we always used to take the train from Aberdeen to London, and then continue later by train from London to Cornwall.

British Rail had a very good train service from Scotland to London, on what is known as the Caledonian Sleeper. It departs Aberdeen railway station at around 9PM every evening. You do not need to queue for one or two hours to pass through airport type security etc. and provided that you arrive at the station five or ten minutes before the departure time, it is a very civilised way to travel.

The sleeper train has cabins with two bunks in each cabin, so you can sleep for the entire journey and arrive in central London at around 6:30AM, where they have showers with fresh towels etc. After boarding the train and finding our cabins, we would take a table in the dining car as the train departed. We would then watch the world go by as we relaxed with a hot meal before I put my three children, Daniel, Jonathan and Tina, to bed. I remember that I would normally have the excellent British Rail cheeseboard washed down with a glass of wine for my supper.

In north-east Scotland, due to the latitude, in mid-summer it does not get dark until after 10PM, and then dawn breaks at about 3AM. However we paid the price for this in mid-winter, as we only had about five hours of daylight then.

Before travelling on to see my father, we would normally spend three days in London taking in the many world-class attractions that the city offers. I remember that the children would spend hours at the Science Museum and the Natural History Museum in South Kensington, but to do these venues justice you would probably have to spend several days there. In my opinion, the only other museum to rival the London Science Museum is the German Science and Technology Museum in Munich, which I have visited on several occasions.

On that day though, I was due to meet Nick Cook. We had arranged to meet at London Zoo in Regent's Park, as the children could roam around happily there and leave Nick and myself free to talk.

We arrived at the zoo just as it opened at 10AM, and I started the kids off in the reptile house adjacent to the main entrance while I waited for Nick. I soon recognised him from his photos on the Internet, and we took a seat at one of the restaurants to begin what would be one of the most fascinating conversations that I have ever had.

He had initially wanted to meet with me to discuss all the aspects of my superconducting turbine that had recently been made public. Nick is an extremely intelligent and well-travelled man. He informed me that he started his career in journalism, but due to his technical training, he eventually worked his way up to become the aviation editor of *Jane's Defence*. As the reader will know, this is the bible for the worldwide defence industry. If you need to know the maximum rate of climb of a MIG 21, or the maximum thrust developed by a certain jet engine, you consult *Jane's Defence*.

After we had gone through the operational principles and design concepts of my superconducting turbine, he informed me that it was a virtual certainty that this equipment would be confiscated by the security services and my operations would be shut down. He therefore told me to make no further contact with him by either email or phone, but instead to communicate only via handwritten letters. He would send his communications to my next-door neighbours, Colin and Anne Appleby, which would make it more difficult for people to eavesdrop on us.

Nick knew far more about the worldwide industrial, defence and military operations than anybody I had previously met. He asked me about subjects such as Red Mercury and other materials that he had encountered during his research into his bestselling book *The Hunt for Zero Point*. During the research for this book he had interviewed many senior figures, including the director of Lockheed Martin's Skunk Works in the USA.

His note of caution regarding our communications was due to the fact that he had previously arranged to meet a senior retired engineer involved in the development of captured Nazi technology pertaining to gravity drive. He flew to the USA for this meeting, but when he phoned the gentleman in question to confirm the meeting time he was told not to come. The meeting which he had previously seemed enthusiastic about would not now occur. Draw your own conclusions.

Regarding the Nazi research related to gravity propulsion, a good deal of his information came from a meeting with another investigative journalist in Poland. After the collapse of the Soviet Union, and Poland coming into the Western sphere of influence and eventually into the European Union, a lot of classified documents seized during World War II were made available. This convinced Nick of the authenticity of many previously reported programmes, and that this technology had been taken by the Allies.

In addition, he informed me that some people believed that gravity drive propulsion had already been used by the Americans in the Northrop Grumman B-2 stealth bomber programme. These warplanes were introduced in 1997 at a reported cost to the US taxpayer of an astonishing $737 million for each aircraft. That was around twenty times the cost of any other warplane the US had previously purchased at that time.

Nick said that from the known thrust of its engines (General Electric F118s), and by applying basic calculations using the aircraft's weight and drag, many aeronautical engineers believed that it could not have left the ground at all with a full fuel and armaments payload. The Americans admitted at the time that the B-2 used a flame jet generator to apply a voltage difference of around four million volts between the leading and trailing edges of the wings. It was also suggested that the refuelling probe on the nose of the aircraft was only installed as people would ask how it could make a non-stop return flight from the USA to Iraq.

Other compelling evidence that the US has on gravity drive came during the first US *Apollo* moon landing. When Armstrong stepped onto the lunar surface, he left deep boot prints in the fine dust that covered the landing area. When the lunar lander finally took off, a video camera, which they had installed on the lunar surface, recorded live footage of the event which was sent back to Earth. Amazingly, despite this dust layer being hit by a supersonic jet of rocket exhaust gas from only two feet away, no dust particles were disturbed. Many now believe that the "rocket motor" was little more than a large inverted egg-cup containing a firework for show.

Nick was very interested in a compound known as Red Mercury at the time. There were rumours that this material had such a high detonation velocity that it could be used to compress a deuterium and tritium core to initiate a nuclear fusion explosion without the need to have a conventional atomic device as the trigger. It was believed that this material needed to be irradiated in a nuclear reactor in order to achieve the desired properties.

Nick knew that during the course of running my business in Aberdeen, I had used both commercial and research nuclear reactors in order to alter the physical properties of the materials that we needed to produce. I needed to manufacture materials such as Silver 110m, a metastable gamma-emitting isotope of silver that we used in shaped explosive charges in order to be able to verify the success of perforating operations for the North Sea oil and gas industry. We also needed to produce Cobalt 60, which emits high-energy (hard) gamma radiation, in order to support pipeline repair and maintenance operations.

When these materials were needed on the UK continental shelf, I produced them in a trigger reactor in East Kilbride, close to Glasgow. The facility there was run by the Scottish Universities Research and Reactor Centre (SURRC). Their reactor could produce thermal neutron flux densities of around 10 to the power 13 neutrons per square centimetre per second. This meant that we did not need to cook the various materials for too long, therefore saving costs.

At that time we also had a considerable amount of work on the Norwegian continental shelf. Due to the difficulty and paperwork involved in transporting radioactive materials across national borders, I produced the isotopes that were required for this work at a facility within Norway. Norway only has two nuclear reactors, both located at Kjeller just outside Oslo, and operated by the Institute for Energy Technique (IFE). I signed a cooperation agreement with the IFE in order to share other technologies with them in return for them irradiating my products for use within Norway.

Unfortunately I had no experience in the use of Red Mercury, and certainly no knowledge of how the properties of this material would be altered by neutron bombardment, so I was not a lot of help to Nick in this particular area.

Later during our meeting, we discussed how business is conducted in many UK cities, and nepotism in the UK in general. It was interesting to hear his perspective on this subject, as my own experiences were gained mainly from my work in Aberdeen.

Aberdeen is considered to be particularly prone to corruption and nepotism due to the city being the oil capital of Europe, and the large sums of money that are changing hands. London is said to be in the same league as Aberdeen because of its position as the financial capital of Europe and the seat of the UK government.

When I started my own business in Aberdeen, I already had my first potential customer lined up. Prior to starting the business I worked for the Schlumberger group, and spent a large proportion of my time visiting their clients and listening to their current technical challenges in order to try to propose solutions. On several occasions, I had to inform clients that we did not have any equipment capable of helping them, but I knew that I could develop equipment to do so.

After starting the company, I initially spent my time on the technical development of the equipment necessary in order to assist my first potential client. Once this equipment was developed, we obtained our first contract with an oil company operating in the North Sea. Following this, I spent the majority of my time either visiting potential new clients, or in developing new equipment to increase the company's portfolio of services.

However I soon learned that a lot of business in Aberdeen is not awarded for technical competence. One of my friends owned a machine shop, and made his money by machining new threads and surfaces on damaged oil field equipment. One day he told me how he had won his latest contract.

He spent his time networking and golfing with the major business players in Aberdeen. He discovered that one oil company had a major consignment of casing in storage, which is very expensive large-diameter tubing that is inserted into wells after a section has been drilled. Some of the threads on this casing had been damaged and needed to be re-machined.

He persuaded one of his golfing buddies, who was the materials manager at the oil company in question, to downgrade the entire consignment to scrap, even though the vast majority of the consignment was undamaged. All of this casing was then shipped to his machine shop, and after less than one week he resold the entire consignment to another oil company. In the process he made more profit than my company initially made in six months. This is just one example, but this type of behaviour goes on all the time due to the amount of money that can be made by unscrupulous local companies and some senior staff in major oil companies operating in the area.

Nepotism is also rife in Aberdeen. One must be careful of the backgrounds of middle-ranking staff that you encounter in many companies, as their fathers are quite often very senior staff or directors in the same company, and may have quite possibly put pressure on the HR departments during the job selection process.

The reputation of Aberdeen recently became so widespread that the city council erected a large new road sign between the airport and the city centre. The sign read *Welcome to Aberdeen, a fair trade city*. Why would the city council feel the need to put this on the main road sign when entering the city, as I have not seen this in other cities that I have visited?

Now let us move to London. I remember two classic cases of alleged nepotism involving senior appointments made by UK government ministers and/or their civil servants. The first case became public after the detention of the director of the British Council's St. Petersburg office by the Russian FSB (formerly the KGB) in 2008. This incident was widely reported in the press at the time. The Director of the British Council was a gentleman named Stephen Kinnock, and it transpired that he was in fact the son of the former British Labour Party leader Neil Kinnock.

I thought that the journalist covering the story that I read was fairly weak. He asked Mr Kinnock Jnr no probing questions. I would have asked him, "Firstly, was the position that you now hold ever advertised prior to you being awarded the job, and if so where?" Secondly I would have asked how many other people applied for this position. Thirdly I would have asked him what particular qualities he thought he had that qualified him for this position above any other candidates. I suspect that the honest answers to these questions would be no, none and none.

His father Neil Kinnock resigned as Labour Party leader after his party had four successive defeats in UK general elections, but was subsequently appointed as a European Commissioner. Soon thereafter his wife Glenys joined him with a position at the European Parliament. However she was soon caught up in an alleged expenses scandal.

The second suspected case involves a gentleman called Chris Patten, aka Baron Patten of Barnes. Chris Patten was the Conservative MP for the small English constituency of Bath. He was thrown out by his constituency following a general election in 1992. He was a close friend and ally to Margaret Thatcher. He was then appointed to the position of Governor General and Commander in Chief of Hong Kong, where he remained until Hong Kong was handed back to the Chinese in 1997.

I was in Hong Kong when his appointment was announced, and I remember the headlines in the local press. They were asking why the British government considered that he had the skill set required to govern over four million people in Hong Kong, when the majority of voters in his small UK constituency did not entrust him to represent them.

During my research carried out while compiling this book, I have spoken to many people working in the fields of industrial technology and military intelligence, as well as many authoritative journalists and publishers. However Nick Cook's research and depth of knowledge in these areas is extremely comprehensive, and I probably learned more from speaking to him that day than I have from any other single source regarding these subjects.

CHAPTER 19

I was woken by my alarm clock. It was another day at university in the 1970s. I was still hungover from the night before, as we had had a pool tournament with other student teams in the campus bar. I looked at my watch hoping that it was a Wednesday, but unfortunately today was a Tuesday. Tuesday for me was the toughest day in the week as we had two double maths lectures back-to-back in the morning.

I graduated from the University of Manchester, and in my first year I stayed at the university halls of residence known as Oak House, which are around a twenty-minute walk from the university complex itself. On Tuesday mornings, we had to attend the same lectures as the pure mathematics undergraduates. In fact forty percent of our lectures in the first year were with the pure mathematics students: if you cannot do the maths, you cannot do the physics.

Wednesdays were my favourite days, as we had geophysics lectures in the mornings. They involved the fundamentals of geoscience, and performing practical exercises such as carrying gravitational anomaly detection equipment up and down between different floors in the building. Even in the 1970s, these instruments were so sensitive that by stretching a quartz crystal within the instrument itself, you could detect the slightest change in the force of the Earth's gravitational field just by going up a few floors within one of the university buildings. Also every Wednesday afternoon was free for sports, so you could relax your brain after lunch.

The physics department itself, in which I attended most of my lectures as a student, had several buildings. The main lecture theatres were in what is known as the Rutherford building. Rutherford, as the reader may recall, was the first person to split the atom, which was one of the major achievements in 20th century physics. Following this he was headhunted by Cambridge University, but the main physics building in Manchester still bears his name.

On Wednesday evenings, I was part of a team competing in quiz nights at one of our local pubs. Our team name was Norfolk & Chance, although we actually did quite well. Each team had four members. The other three in our team covered a broad spectrum of knowledge. The eldest was a local plumber in his thirties. He was a sports fanatic, and there was very little that he did not know in this area. The next was a lecturer in history from the university, who also knew a lot about classics and the arts. The final member was a flaky barmaid from the pub itself. Although no towering intellect, she knew pretty much everything about pop music and soap operas, and was a great help. So between us, we had most of the bases covered.

I managed most of the science questions. Sometimes our team was the only one to answer certain questions correctly. On one occasion a question was "define the value of 3.877 raised to the power zero". Sounds hard, but any number raised to the power zero has a value of one. Another question I remember was about imaginary numbers. These are numbers that do not exist, as when you square a negative imaginary number its value is still negative. It may sound stupid, but you need them to build equations to resolve some problems in science. If you have got the maths right, they should all cancel out in the end and you are back in the real world.

As I was studying for joint honours degrees in physics and geology, I attended many lectures and practical sessions in the geology department on the complex. These were often quite amusing, as many female students took geology as part of a degree in something that they used to call general studies. This, in my opinion, is pretty much the same as a string of O-levels, and I did not understand why they would award a degree for this level of knowledge.

I think it was probably because the students on this course had wealthy parents who did not want their children to stack the shelves at Tesco, so they sent them to university to study one of the few courses in which they were able to be enrolled. I believe that today this has been replaced by a course known as media studies.

I think that the university system in England when I was a student was considerably better than the system today under which my children are being educated. In the 1970s, almost all freshmen were given places in university accommodation to help them find their feet and make friends. After this, you had to make your own arrangements for your accommodation for the remaining years.

Although things were not easy when I was an undergraduate, I think that they are considerably more difficult today. When I started at university, provided that you achieved the grades stipulated for your initial enrolment, and passed all of your terminal exams at the end of each academic year, you automatically had your tuition fees paid, and received a grant from the local education authority to cover your basic living costs. I still have two children at university. Today in England, the students are required to pay their own tuition fees, in addition to finding the money to cover all of their accommodation and living costs.

There are many young people I have known virtually all of their lives, from the time that they were bouncing around on the trampoline with my own children, right up to the time they finished high school. Many of these kids were very smart, but did not go to university simply because their parents could not pay for it, or because they would not take out a student loan and start their working lives many tens of thousands of pounds in debt.

I think this is a great shame, as if the UK wants to compete with the Americans, Germans and Japanese etc., our young people must have a world-class education. Since leaving university, I have paid UK income tax which probably amounts to more than one hundred times the cost of my education to the British government, and I think that their current education policy is extremely short-sighted.

After the first year, two friends and I found accommodation in a high-rise apartment complex close to the university in Moss Side. It was pretty grim in those days, but I have since been told that today if you are an unknown face and enter Moss Side you need to be carrying an Uzi. Following one traumatic year there, we moved to another district of Manchester called Levenshulme.

I remember one winter's evening when we didn't have the cash to go out, we were all huddled around the electric heater watching TV. That evening, we were watching a programme called *Whicker's World*. It was about the globetrotting journalist, Alan Whicker, who visited various destinations and reported on the lifestyles of the rich and famous. The episode we were watching was a classic, and it made us formulate our holiday plans for the following summer.

He was reporting on West Palm Beach, Florida. It transpired that there were many wealthy retired American couples living there, and the husbands often dropped dead from a heart attack or similar soon after the couple had retired. Their widows then often trawled the beach area in a Rolls Royce, in order to pick up handsome young men to escort them to social engagements. He reported that these young men were often given a Porsche or Ferrari for their efforts. A good deal, we thought. We could not take a car home as the Americans drive on the wrong side of the road, but hey, we could still sell one. Being a bunch of poor and naive students, we thought that this would work for us, and our holiday plans were hatched.

One of the beauties about being a student is that, on our particular course, we had twenty-seven weeks of term time and twenty-five weeks of vacation. When the summer vacation started, we all worked for two months in order to earn as much money as possible, and then purchased the cheapest airline tickets possible to Florida. We all hung out in West Palm Beach for two weeks, but never even got a bite. God bless the young and naive.

The main reason that I am reminiscing about my student years is that my youngest son is currently studying for an MSc in physics at the University of Aberdeen. It is quite astonishing that some of the things he is being taught today fundamentally contradict what I was taught at university thirty-five years ago.

For example, I was taught that there were four fundamental forces in the universe. They were the strong nuclear force, the weak nuclear force, gravity and electromagnetism. Today physics undergraduates are taught that there are probably only three. This is because physicists today believe that electromagnetism and gravity are connected, although the exact mechanism of this connection has yet to be proven.

Since the 1970s, our knowledge of science has continued to expand at an exponential rate. When I was at university I did question some of the concepts that we were taught. One of the most unsatisfactory was that there was no coherent explanation of the properties of light. Sometimes the behaviour of light could only be explained if it was a wave form, and sometimes its behaviour could only be explained if it was a photon (a particle with mass).

In the 1920s, scientists knew that there would be a forthcoming total eclipse of the sun observable from Australia. Many scientific missions headed to Australia prior to this, to make recordings and observations of the eclipse. During the eclipse, many stars were visible which were known to be directly behind the sun. If the light was travelling in a straight line, as it is supposed to do in a vacuum, it would not be possible to observe the stars, but they could.

This phenomenon was explained away as light being transmitted by photons, which were particles that had mass. As such they would bend as they travelled around the sun to the observer on Earth. This was called gravity lensing at the time, and was due to the photons being affected by the gravity of the sun and therefore having their paths through space bent.

However it was difficult to reconcile this with Einstein's general theory of relativity. Einstein stated that as a particle accelerates towards the speed of light its mass increases. In order to obtain the speed of light, a particle must be massless, as if not it would have an infinite mass at the speed of light, which is obviously impossible. If a photon is massless, how is it affected by a gravitational field?

Another conundrum that I could not resolve at school and university in the 1970s was the diffraction pattern experiments that we studied. I am sure that most of you can recall the experiments we all did at school involving shining monochromatic light onto two slits, and observing the interference pattern on the far side of the slits. This at the time was explained in the same way as ripples on a pond resulting from two stones being thrown into the water simultaneously, and the waves combining to create a series of peaks and troughs.

However since the 1970s, experiments have been performed repeatedly, demonstrating that a single electron fired at a pair of slits will produce a diffraction pattern on the far side. An explanation was offered by Heisenberg's uncertainty principle. This states that as a particle gets smaller its position is more difficult to establish. Once you get down to the atomic and subatomic levels, a single particle will take all possible paths simultaneously, and therefore produce the diffraction pattern.

Some concepts in physics are difficult to understand. I think this is because they defy our common sense. However common sense is only gained as a result of the experiences that we have built up by observing the world around us throughout our lives. As we have no experience at all of events occurring at the atomic and subatomic levels, it is understandable that we cannot apply common sense to the observed behaviour of these particles.

The particle/wave duality of light is currently better addressed by quantum physics, but there are still unanswered questions.

Today, physicists are talking about particles named bosons. It is currently believed that many fundamental particles are in fact bosons at lower energy states, and that bosons are the fundamental building blocks of the universe. This theory is still being researched, and at the time of writing remains unproven.

I would now like to discuss an incident that took place a number of years ago regarding UFO sightings in the airspace over Belgium. This was widely reported in the press at the time. I personally do not believe in extra-terrestrials having visited us from other star systems. I believe that this is just a convenient cover story for the advanced and secret activities of the US military.

We already know that the Americans looted the Skoda works near Pilsen in 1945. Not only did they take the entire hoard of top-secret scientific work and research of the Nazis, but they also got virtually all of their top scientists as well. This vast pool of advanced technology was then shipped back to the US.

We know that gravity can be artificially manipulated, as attested to by the many repeatable experiments performed and patents that have been awarded in this area. However many credible witnesses in the 1940s reported that the Nazis had developed this propulsion system to the point where large disks were observed flying silently in the skies around western Czechoslovakia.

As the Americans have been in possession of this technology for about seventy years now, it is not difficult to imagine the advancements that they achieved considering that the Germans reached this point after a matter of just a few years' research.

Many people who believe that extra-terrestrial beings have visited Earth point to examples such as the construction of the pyramids, and say that the ancient people of that time did not have the technology to build such structures on a perfectly level base etc. I cannot agree with this, and many of the assertions made can be explained away simply.

In order to make a perfectly level base for a pyramid, you simply need to mark out your square on the ground and then dig a ditch along the edges of the square. If the ditch is then lined with clay and filled with water, the base can be adjusted until the level of water in the ditch is the same all around the periphery. This is one of the basic techniques that some bricklayers still use today in order to build level walls.

Now let us return to the discussion of the Belgian UFO incident. This occurrence was again observed by many credible witnesses from many different locations, and was considered serious enough that the Belgian Air Force scrambled F-16 fighters to investigate. The various eyewitness accounts corroborated each other, and people observed these objects accelerating from stationary to supersonic speeds in just a second or two. They were also observed to make almost ninety-degree turns virtually instantaneously while travelling at supersonic speeds.

This incident was explained away by the authorities as atmospheric phenomena, and the corroborating radar evidence was allegedly due to malfunctioning equipment. When this incident was subsequently investigated by knowledgeable journalists and scientists in this field, it was obvious that the explanation offered by the authorities was completely untenable.

Recordings of the radar tracking data of the incident were examined in great detail. Data was obtained from one civilian ground-based air traffic control radar, and also from a military ground-based radar which used a completely different system and was made by a different manufacturer. In addition the air-to-air interception radar data from the warplanes scrambled during this incident was also evaluated. Again this was yet another type of radar system from a third manufacturer, but the data from all three separate radar systems matched perfectly.

I believe that the only realistic explanation of this incident was the testing of a highly advanced type of aerial vehicle. We already know that gravity drive propulsion exists, and the huge accelerations and violent high-speed turns recorded would be quite possible provided that this system had been developed in order to act as an inertia cancelling system.

Should an air vehicle attempt to perform any acceleration or a change in direction that would generate forces of hundreds of G, this would obviously destroy any conventional aircraft and kill any pilot using our current disclosed understanding of materials, science and medicine. However if a second gravity drive is on board the craft, and instantaneously creates a 100 G field against the craft and its occupants as a 100 G turn is executed, the aerial vehicle and any occupants would feel no effect from this. It is only a small step in terms of theoretical physics to develop an inertia cancelling system from an artificial gravity propulsion system.

CHAPTER 20

The one thing in particular that confirms to me the secretive nature and disinformation that has, for a long time, surrounded government activities can be summed up by one word that has recently entered the English language in a new context. The word is "redempted".

In both Europe and the US, recent legislation has been enacted regarding the release of information to the public under the Freedom of Information Act. This obliges government authorities to release any known information that is legitimately requested by journalists, researchers and other groups.

The problem with this is that they get around the legislation by one of two means. Firstly, if no known information on the topic requested has been released previously, an information request will normally be returned saying that no records on this subject exist. The second method is if information is known to exist, the information is released to comply with the law but it has been redempted. This means that much of the information released has been blacked out and is therefore impossible to read. However the department releasing the information has complied with the letter of the law, but certainly not spirit.

There are ways of getting around this. Much of this information was originally typed in Times New Roman script. This script compresses or expands the text depending on the length of the individual characters. For example, "I" takes up the shortest line width, and "W" takes up the longest. By using this analysis of the text, it is possible to reinstate some of the redempted information.

During my research for this book, I made many requests concerning any data available regarding numerous different topics. When the redempted information arrived I used this approach, but I also took the blacked-out papers received to friends of mine who were working inside the atomic energy and weapons programmes during the 1960s and 1970s. These scientists are now retired and in their eighties, but they were able to fill in the great majority of the information that had been censored. Although they were all originally bound by the Official Secrets Act, I do not think that the UK government would gain any public sympathy by taking any action against such elderly gentleman for releasing information that is now decades old.

Before we get into this, the other amusing phrase that the British government has recently introduced into the language is "fiscal easing". This is apparently the politically correct way to disguise the fact that you are printing banknotes as fast as you can in order to temporarily get yourself out of the brown stuff. It didn't work for the Nazis (just look what happened to the Reich's Mark), but it does sound more palatable to the public than bailing yourself out of a hole by printing money.

Everyone knows about the Trinity nuclear tests and the atomic bombs dropped on Hiroshima and Nagasaki, but the subsequent development of nuclear weapons has been the subject of Western disinformation for decades.

Throughout my life, I have listened to and read reports in the British media attempting to convince the public that we were way ahead of the Soviets in terms of advanced technology. As the years progressed, and I was in possession of the full facts relating to the cases reported at the time, it was apparent that these early press releases were disinformation of the highest calibre.

The West has always claimed that the Soviets and Russians are the masters of disinformation, but from my own observations and my interviews with retired former government nuclear scientists, I believe that the Western governments are every bit as guilty.

We all know that the CIA used the U2 spy plane to detect the Soviet missiles being located in Cuba with a capability of striking the US mainland. This event was probably the closest that the world has been to nuclear war since the development of the atomic bomb. What transpired later, and was not reported at the time, was that the Soviet action in Cuba was in response to the US positioning similar short-range nuclear missiles in Turkey, capable of striking the Soviet Union. This important piece of information conveniently went unreported at the time, and the Western media declared a great victory for JFK.

Another very significant piece of history that was never reported in the UK press, and I believe has never been publicly disclosed before this book was published, is the development of Delta Plutonium. During the 1960s and 1970s the Western public were continually assured that we were well in advance of the Soviet Union in terms of both weapons technology and delivery systems.

The Soviet Union successfully tested its first atomic bomb in 1949. They then successfully tested their first hydrogen bomb in 1953, which was only one year after the first successful test of a hydrogen bomb in the United States.

The difference between the early atomic bombs and the hydrogen bomb is as follows. The early atomic bombs were constructed using two targets of either uranium or plutonium, which were made to combine as a result of a conventional high explosive detonation. Both uranium and plutonium have what is known as a critical mass. This means the mass at which spontaneous fission (detonation) will occur when a sufficient quantity of either fissile material is combined.

Therefore the two targets must both be below this critical mass within the weapon, otherwise it would detonate during construction. The hydrogen bomb uses a completely different principle. It uses a conventional atomic explosion to compress a core containing the hydrogen isotopes of deuterium and tritium. The compression within the detonating bomb causes the nuclei of the hydrogen isotopes to fuse into helium, releasing huge amounts of energy.

This principle, the nuclear fusion of hydrogen, is exactly how energy is created within the sun and other stars. As the core size of a hydrogen bomb will not affect the critical mass that limited the size of conventional atomic weapons, the explosive power that a hydrogen bomb can generate is virtually unlimited.

After the Soviet Union detonated its first hydrogen bomb in 1953, the Americans overflew the detonation site with a U2 spy plane. They collected atmospheric samples for analysis. They discovered that the atmosphere around the blast site contained a high level of the element osmium. Osmium is the densest material naturally occurring within the Earth's crust. At the time, the Americans believed that the Soviets surrounded the core of the bomb with an osmium jacket in order to concentrate the fusion reaction, and to increase the yield of the detonation.

The US and British believed at the time that any highly dense material could be used for this purpose, and that the Soviets had chosen to use osmium only because significant deposits of this element are available in the Ural mountain range.

Osmium is normally found alloyed with noble metals such as platinum, gold and silver, and also as the compound osmium tetroxide. Osmium tetroxide is a toxic non-metallic substance that is used as a solution in biology, known as osmium acid, for staining fat cells for examination under a microscope.

The information obtained from this U2 mission was shared with the British Atomic Weapons Research Establishment (AWRE) at Aldermaston, and the British agreed with the conclusions of the Americans at that time. It took several decades before the true reason for the Soviet use of osmium was discovered by the West.

Plutonium is a very unusual metallic element. Virtually all other metals remain as a solid with a certain crystalline structure until they are heated to their melting point. They then become a liquid. Plutonium does not behave in this way. When plutonium is heated, and as a certain temperature is reached, instead of melting it just changes its crystalline structure (slumps) and then re-crystallises as a new solid structure as the temperature continues to rise.

It took another thirty years for the British and Americans to discover that the best usable and temperature-stable form of weapons grade plutonium was a special alloy known as Delta plutonium. Delta plutonium is an alloy of plutonium and osmium. Yet during the Cold War the Western governments deceived the public into thinking that we were so far ahead of the Soviet Union in terms of weapons technology.

Today, plutonium/osmium binary alloy phase diagrams and allotropic transformation data with orthorhombic, face-centred cubic and other crystalline transformations etc. can be purchased from the web.

Plutonium has six crystal structures. At room temperature, pure plutonium is hard and brittle and difficult to machine. In addition to its temperature stability, Delta plutonium with its cubic crystal structure may be cast and machined readily.

My source for this information was a retired UK government scientist who attended the 1985 Geneva conference on the peaceful uses of atomic energy. He quoted to me:

"The Russians published a great quantity of information regarding plutonium alloys that amazed the UK and US with their details. We did not use osmium for this purpose, and at the time the composition of our attempts to make a stabilised alloy was a closely guarded secret."

Probably the greatest scientific and engineering advances that I have seen since the 1970s have been in the area of semiconductors and computing. When I was at school in the early 1970s, I had never seen an electronic calculator. We had to bring our slide rules to the maths and science classes, and if we forgot our slide rules, we received a rap across the knuckles and were issued with log tables.

I remember the first time that my father bought an electronic calculator to show us I was absolutely amazed. My father worked at a major nuclear research facility, and they had just purchased these calculators for around $400 each (and that was forty years ago). They were only capable of performing the four basic mathematical functions, and were about half the size of a typewriter with cold cathode display tubes as opposed to using a screen display. Today people give away calculators the size of credit cards that can perform these functions and more just for opening a bank account.

It is generally accepted that the first electronic calculator/computer was the Colossus machine built by the code breakers at Bletchley Park during World War II. Its purpose was to help in decoding the highly complex Enigma cipher used by the Germans at the time. The scientists who worked on this project summed it up by saying that instead of looking for a needle in a thousand haystacks, with Colossus they were now looking for a needle in just one, but still a mind-boggling task as the Enigma cipher settings were changed so frequently.

The Germans believed this code to be unbreakable, but it was successfully broken by the scientists at Bletchley Park. Winston Churchill famously said that the data provided by Bletchley Park probably shortened World War II by two years, and saved millions of lives. For the readers who have not seen the film *Enigma*, it is enthralling and factually based, and I highly recommend watching this film.

By the early 1980s, the advance in semiconductors and computers had reached the point where their use was becoming commonplace in the work and office environment. When I started my first business in 1984, the computers that we initially purchased were the Vectra model manufactured by Hewlett-Packard. At that time, IBM pretty much had the market cornered with their PC AT desktop computer.

These were fairly bulky machines that still used cathode ray tubes for the display. However this machine became the industry standard at that time, as you could easily open it up and there were many spare slots on the motherboard to insert additional cards for the specific tasks that you wished the computer to perform. At that time, I remember that for a Vectra computer fitted with the additional data processing and signal evaluation cards that we required, the cost was around $15,000 per machine.

Today, for about $1,000 you can purchase a laptop or tablet with the computing power and speed of a roomful of 1980's mainframe computers that would have been cutting-edge at the time. In addition to the vast increase in clock speed (computing speed) that computers gained over the years, I think the most amazing advances have been made in data storage and memory capacity.

All 1980's office computers had extremely limited memory, and to backup anything you needed to use the internal 3.5 inch floppy disk drive. Each disc had a paltry memory of only 1.44 MB. Therefore in addition to your computer, you needed to purchase an external zip drive if you wanted to backup and store any reasonable amount of data. These drives had an initial capacity of 100 MB, and then subsequently 200 MB on each removable disk.

The zip drives were soon overtaken by the development of the rewritable CD/DVD. These drives were then fitted to nearly all computers, rendering the previous internal floppy disk drives and the external zip drives obsolete. However with the massive advance in the memory capacity available on silicon chips, it would not be long before all mechanical drives were effectively obsolete.

Today most people back everything up on USB flash drives. The memory capacity of these sticks would have been unthinkable just ten or fifteen years ago. You can now purchase a flash drive the size of your fingertip which has a memory capacity upwards of 1,000 GB. Even five years ago, most new and fairly expensive computers had nothing like this memory capacity available.

I know that today a lot of people complain because when you buy software with your new PC, tablet or whatever you are not supplied with any type of backup should your system crash. I believe that the software manufacturers have taken advantage of the phasing out of CD/DVD data storage. These days, although you buy a nice-looking plastic box which could contain a disc (to try to justify the hundreds of dollars that you have just spent the software), all you get inside the box is a piece of cardboard with an "authorisation code", which is required in order to make the software work.

The software is now preloaded onto the device prior to purchase, and then you need to get online and enter your authorisation code to activate it. The problems start when your computer completely freezes, and the hard drive within the computer must be reformatted in many cases, or even replaced. I have heard that the term coined by the computer hardware manufacturers for this is "built-in redundancy". This new phrase is almost as good as "fiscal easing", aka printing money.

Should you try to download the originally installed software from the web, it will not be activated as you have already used the original code supplied with the software. Helpline phone numbers seem to be permanently busy, and your emails to their website go unanswered. As you have no CD/DVD backup of the programs, you are often forced to repurchase the software that you have already paid for. I can only imagine the size of the bonuses paid to the software engineers who thought up this piece of marketing genius.

CHAPTER 21

Some of the greatest advances during the last few decades have been made in both terrestrial and space telescope technology. This has greatly increased our investigative power in attempting to understand more about gravity generation and interaction, particle physics, and our understanding of the universe in general.

Telescopes are normally classified by the wavelengths they can detect. The main groups are:

1. X-ray telescopes, using shorter wavelengths than ultraviolet light
2. Ultraviolet telescopes, using shorter wavelengths than visible light
3. Optical telescopes, using visible light
4. Infrared telescopes, using longer wavelengths than visible light
5. Sub-millimetre telescopes, using longer wavelengths than infrared light

As wavelengths become longer, it becomes easier to use antenna technology to detect the electromagnetic radiation. The near-infrared can be handled much like visible light, however in the far-infrared and sub-millimetre range, the telescopes used are known as radio telescopes. When I was an undergraduate in Manchester, the largest UK radio telescope at that time was at Jodrell Bank, and operated by our physics department.

The amount of data that scientists have collected using these various different types of telescopes is huge. When Einstein first postulated his special theory of relativity and subsequently his general theory of relativity, he did not have access to the type of data available today. Einstein postulated that gravity is caused by the bending of space time. Although this is still believed to be one cause of gravity, it does not explain the full picture that we can now see.

Using modern telescopes, we can observe cosmic objects unknown to Newton and Einstein, such as twin neutron stars. These can produce gravity waves that radiate out through space and can be detected on Earth. At the time of writing, physicists are discussing string theory, and the associated gravity waves that strings generate. Also being discussed is the possibility of gravity being transmitted by a particle dubbed the graviton. The jury is still out regarding these theories, but we are gaining more information every year.

There are, however, objects in the cosmos that we still know very little about. Black holes for example are objects with such an enormous density that they suck in anything within their vicinity. Around the periphery of a black hole is a region that is known as an event horizon. This is the boundary beyond which no object cannot escape the gravitational force of the black hole. It is not even possible to observe the events taking place inside the event horizon.

It is believed that a singularity lies at the centre of each black hole. A singularity is a point at which space time is distorted so violently that it is meaningless, and space time is effectively pinched out.

We will now have a brief discussion about space time. Science today accepts that space and time are basically the same thing, hence the phrase "space time". As an object accelerates faster towards the speed of light, not only does its mass increase, but time as observed by that object slows down. Perception of space time is dependent on the frame of reference of the observer.

To understand this, imagine a passenger on a fast train bouncing a tennis ball up and down against the floor. Another passenger in the same carriage would observe the motion of the ball to be vertical, covering the short distance between the hand and the floor of the carriage. However, if this same motion was observed by another person who was standing on a station platform as the train passed by, from their point of reference the ball would appear to be travelling in a long diagonal motion and covering a much longer path.

Many years ago, I used to get into some interesting discussions with one of my wife's best friends regarding science. She was often sitting in our lounge drinking coffee when I returned from an overseas trip. When I joined their conversations, I sometimes found it quite amusing. She often tried to impress me with her almost non-existent knowledge of science, and her peer group with her supposedly green credentials.

On one occasion, she had just purchased an electric-powered car, a vehicle which none of her friends at that time owned. She would bleat on about how environmentally friendly she was, as her car produced zero emissions. I said, "Okay, but where do you think the electricity to recharge the batteries comes from?" She said, "Oh, for green cars it comes from solar power, wind power and only renewable resources."

"Okay, but when do you normally recharge the batteries in your car?" I said. "Oh, at nighttime of course," she replied, so I suggested that solar power was not available at nighttime. She then replied that it obviously used wind power then. She really did need to be led by the nose. I then asked her where the power came from on a windless night. At that point she realised that she was painting herself into a corner. Surprisingly she did not like me very much.

In physics, string theory is a theoretical framework in which the point-like particle is replaced by one-dimensional objects called strings. String theory aims to explain all types of observed elementary particles using quantum states of these strings. In addition to the particles postulated by the standard model of particle physics, string theory naturally incorporates gravity, and so is a candidate for a theory of everything, a self-contained mathematical model that describes all fundamental forces and forms of matter. Besides this hypothesised role in particle physics, string theory is now widely used as a theoretical tool in physics, and has shed light on many aspects of quantum field theory and quantum gravity.

The earliest version of string theory, called bosonic string theory, incorporated only the class of particles known as bosons, although this theory developed into superstring theory, which postulates that a connection a "super symmetry" exists between bosons and the class of particles called fermions. String theory requires the existence of extra spatial dimensions for its mathematical consistency. In realistic physical models constructed from string theory, these extra dimensions are typically compacted to extremely small scales.

String theory was first studied in the 1970s as a theory of the strong nuclear force before being abandoned in favour of the theory of quantum chromo-dynamics. Subsequently, it was realised that the very properties that made string theory unsuitable as a theory of nuclear physics made it an outstanding candidate for a quantum theory of gravity.

After five consistent versions of string theory were developed, it was realised in the mid-1990s that these theories could be obtained as different limits of a conjectured eleven-dimensional theory called M-theory. Many theoretical physicists believe that string theory is a step towards the correct fundamental description of nature. This is because string theory allows for the consistent combination of quantum field theory and general relativity, agrees with general insights in quantum gravity such as the holographic principle and black hole thermodynamics, and has passed many non-trivial checks of its internal consistency.

According to Hawking, M-theory is the only candidate for a complete theory of the universe. Other physicists, such as Richard Feynman, Roger Penrose and Sheldon Lee Glashow, have criticised string theory for not providing novel experimental predictions at accessible energy scales and say that it is a failure as a theory of everything.

The starting point for string theory is the idea that the point-like particles of elementary particle physics can also be modelled as one-dimensional objects called strings. According to string theory, strings can oscillate in many ways. On distance scales larger than the string radius, each oscillation mode gives rise to a different species of particle, with its mass, charge and other properties determined by the string's dynamics. Splitting and recombination of strings correspond to particle emission and absorption, giving rise to the interactions between particles. An analogy for strings' modes of vibration is a guitar string's production of multiple distinct musical notes. In this analogy, different notes correspond to different particles.

In string theory, one of the modes of oscillation of the string corresponds to a massless, spin-2 particle. Such a particle is called a graviton since it mediates a force which has the properties of gravity. Since string theory is believed to be a mathematically consistent quantum mechanical theory, the existence of this graviton state implies that string theory is a theory of quantum gravity.

String theory includes both open strings, which have two distinct endpoints, and closed strings, which form a complete loop. The two types of string behave in slightly different ways, yielding different particle types. For example, all string theories have closed string graviton modes, but only open strings can correspond to the particles known as photons. Because the two ends of an open string can always meet and connect, forming a closed string, all string theories contain closed strings.

The earliest string model, the bosonic string, incorporated only the class of particles known as bosons. This model describes, at low enough energies, a quantum gravity theory, which also includes (if open strings are incorporated as well) gauge bosons such as the photon. However, this model has problems. What is most significant is that the theory has a fundamental instability, believed to result in the decay (at least partially) of space time itself. In addition, as the name implies, the spectrum of particles contains only bosons, particles which, like the photon, obey particular rules of behaviour.

Roughly speaking, bosons are the constituents of radiation, but not of matter, which is made of fermions. Investigating how a string theory may include fermions led to the invention of super symmetry, a mathematical relation between bosons and fermions. String theories that include fermionic vibrations are now known as superstring theories. Several kinds have been described, but all are now thought to be different limits of a theory called M-theory.

Since string theory incorporates all of the fundamental interactions, including gravity, many physicists hope that it fully describes our universe, making it a theory of everything. One of the goals of current research in string theory is to find a solution of the theory that is quantitatively identical with the standard model, with a small cosmological constant, containing dark matter and a plausible mechanism for cosmic inflation. It is not yet known whether string theory has such a solution, nor is it known how much freedom the theory allows to choose the details.

One of the challenges of string theory is that the full theory does not yet have a satisfactory definition in all circumstances. The scattering of strings is most straightforwardly defined using the techniques of perturbation theory, but it is not known in general how to define string theory non-perturbativley. It is also not clear as to whether there is any principle by which string theory selects its vacuum state, the space time configuration that determines the properties of our universe.

The motion of a point-like particle can be described by drawing a graph of its position with respect to time. The resulting picture depicts the world line of the particle in space time. In an analogous way, one can draw a graph depicting the progress of a string as time passes. The string, which looks like a small line by itself, will sweep out a two-dimensional surface known as the world sheet. The different string modes (giving rise to different particles, such as the photon or graviton) appear as waves on this surface.

A closed string looks like a small loop, so its world sheet will look like a pipe. An open string looks like a segment with two endpoints, so its world sheet will look like a strip. In a more mathematical language, these are both Riemann surfaces, the strip having a boundary and the pipe none.

The interactions in the subatomic world can be described in two ways, either as world lines of point-like particles in the standard model, or as world sheets swept up by closed strings in string theory.

Strings can join and split. This is reflected by the form of their world sheet, or more precisely, by its topology. For example, if a closed string splits, its world sheet will look like a single pipe splitting into two pipes. This topology is often referred to as a pair of pants. If a closed string splits and its two parts later reconnect, its world sheet will look like a single pipe splitting in two and then reconnecting, which also looks like a torus connected to two pipes (one representing the incoming string, and the other representing the outgoing one). An open string doing the same thing will have a world sheet that looks like an annulus connected to two strips.

In quantum mechanics, one computes the probability for a point particle to propagate from one point to another by summing certain quantities called probability amplitudes. Each amplitude is associated with a different world line of the particle. This process of summing amplitudes over all possible world lines is called path integration. In string theory, one computes probabilities in a similar way, by summing quantities associated with the world sheets joining an initial string configuration to a final configuration. It is in this sense that string theory extends quantum field theory, replacing point particles by strings. As in quantum field theory, the classical behaviour of fields is determined by an action functional, which in string theory can be either the Nambu–Goto action or the Polyakov action.

An intriguing feature of string theory is that it predicts extra dimensions. In classical string theory the number of dimensions is not fixed by any consistency criterion. However, to make a consistent quantum theory, string theory is required to live in a space time of the so-called "critical dimension": we must have twenty-six space time dimensions for the bosonic string and ten for the superstring. This is necessary to ensure the vanishing of the conformal anomaly of the world sheet conformal field theory.

Modern understanding indicates that there exist less trivial ways of satisfying this criterion. Cosmological solutions exist in a wider variety of dimensionalities, and these different dimensions are related by dynamical transitions. The dimensions are more precisely different values of the "effective central charge", a count of degrees of freedom that reduces to dimensionality in weakly curved regimes.

One such theory is the eleven-dimensional M-theory, which requires space time to have eleven dimensions, as opposed to the usual three spatial dimensions and the fourth dimension of time. The original string theories from the 1980s describe special cases of M-theory where the eleventh dimension is a very small circle or a line, and if these formulations are considered as fundamental, then string theory requires ten dimensions.

But the theory also describes universes like ours, with four observable space time dimensions, as well as universes with up to ten flat space dimensions, and also cases where the position in some of the dimensions is described by a complex number rather than a real number. The notion of space time dimension is not fixed in string theory: it is best thought of as different in different circumstances.

Nothing in Maxwell's theory of electromagnetism or Einstein's theory of relativity makes this kind of prediction.

These theories require physicists to insert the number of dimensions manually and arbitrarily, and this number is fixed and independent of potential energy.

String theory allows one to relate the number of dimensions to scalar potential energy. In technical terms, this happens because a gauge anomaly exists for every separate number of predicted dimensions, and the gauge anomaly can be counteracted by including nontrivial potential energy into equations to solve motion. Furthermore, the absence of potential energy in the "critical dimension" explains why flat space time solutions are possible. This can be better understood by noting that a photon included in a consistent theory (technically, a particle carrying a force related to an unbroken gauge symmetry) must be massless. The mass of the photon that is predicted by string theory depends on the energy of the string mode that represents the photon.

This energy includes a contribution from the Casimir effect, namely from quantum fluctuations in the string. The size of this contribution depends on the number of dimensions, since for a larger number of dimensions there are more possible fluctuations in the string position. Therefore, the photon in flat space time will be massless – and the theory consistent – only for a particular number of dimensions. When the calculation is done, the critical dimensionality is not four as one may expect (three axes of space and one of time).

The subset of X is equal to the relation of photon fluctuations in a linear dimension. Flat space string theories are twenty-six-dimensional in the bosonic case, while superstring and M-theories turn out to involve ten or eleven dimensions for flat solutions. In bosonic string theories, the twenty-six dimensions come from the Polyakov equation. Starting from any dimension greater than four, it is necessary to consider how these are reduced.

Gravitons are postulated because of the great success of quantum field theory (in particular, the Standard Model) at modelling the behaviour of all other known forces of nature as being mediated by elementary particles: electromagnetism by the photon, the strong interaction by the gluons and the weak interaction by the W and Z bosons. The hypothesis is that the gravitational interaction is likewise mediated by another elementary particle, dubbed the graviton. In the classical limit, the theory would reduce to general relativity and conform to Newton's law of gravitation in the weak field limit.

However, attempts to extend the Standard Model with gravitons have run into serious theoretical difficulties at high energies (processes with energies close to or above the Planck scale) because of infinities arising due to quantum effects. Since classical general relativity and quantum mechanics are incompatible at such energies, from a theoretical point of view the present situation is not tenable. Some proposed models of quantum gravity attempt to address these issues, but these are speculative theories.

As recently as the 19th century, many people thought that it would be impossible to determine the chemical composition of the stars. Since then, physicists have proved them wrong by using spectroscopy.

The word spectrum is used today to mean a display of electromagnetic radiation as a function of wavelength. A spectrum originally meant a phantom or apparition, but Isaac Newton introduced a new meaning in 1671, when he reported his experiment of decomposing the white sunlight into colours using a prism. Several related words, such as spectroscopy (the study of spectra) and spectrograph have since been introduced into the English language.

You can be a spectroscopist (a person who studies spectra) as well. When you see a rainbow, or use a prism on a beam of sunlight to project a band of colours onto a screen or a wall, it will probably appear as if the change of colours is gradual, and the change in intensity of the light of different colours is also gradual. We use the word continuum to describe spectra that change gradually like this.

There are also discrete features, called emission lines or absorption lines depending on whether they are brighter or fainter than the neighbouring continuum. You can use a prism on candlelight or some special light bulbs to observe these effects.

Most bright astronomical objects shine because they are hot. In such cases, the continuum they emit tells us what the temperature is. Here is a very rough guide.

Temperature (K)	Predominant Radiation	Astronomical examples
600	Infrared	Planets and warm dust
6,000	Optical	Photosphere of stars
60,000	UV	Photosphere of hot stars
600,000	Soft X-rays	Corona of the sun
6,000,000	X-rays	Coronae of active stars

We can learn a lot more from the spectral lines than from the continuum, and can actually determine the chemical composition of stars.

During the first half of the 19th century, scientists such as John Herschel, Fox Talbot and William Swan studied the spectra of different chemical elements in flames. Gradually, the idea that each element produces a set of characteristic emission lines was established. Each element has several prominent, and many lesser, emission lines in a characteristic pattern. Sodium, for example, has two prominent yellow lines (the so-called D lines) at 589.0 and 589.6 nm – any sample that contains sodium (such as table salt) can be easily recognised using this pair of lines. All of the elements have this type of unique "bar code".

Joseph Fraunhofer is the most famous and probably also the most important contributor to studies in this field, and revealed absorption lines (dark lines against the brighter continuum). The precise origin of these "Fraunhofer lines", as we call them today, remained in doubt for many years until discoveries made by Gustav Kirchhoff. He announced that the same substance can either produce emission lines (when a hot gas is emitting its own light) or absorption lines (when a light from a brighter, and usually hotter, source is shone through it). Now scientists had the means to determine the chemical composition of stars through spectroscopy.

One of the most dramatic triumphs of early spectroscopy during the 19th century was the discovery of helium. An emission line at 587.6 nm was first observed in the solar corona during the eclipse of 18th August 1868, although the precise wavelength was difficult to establish at the time due to the short observation using temporary set-ups of instruments transported to Asia.

Later, Norman Lockyer used a new technique and managed to observe solar prominences without waiting for an eclipse. He noted a line with the precise wavelength (587.6 nm), and knew that this must be helium. Today, from the data collected by our advanced space telescopes, we know that helium is the second most abundant element in the universe. We also now know that the most abundant element is hydrogen.

However, this fact was not obvious at first. Many years of both observational and theoretical works culminated when Cecilia Payne published her PhD thesis entitled *Stellar Atmospheres*. In this early work, she utilised many excellent spectra taken by Harvard observers, and measured the intensities of 134 different lines from eighteen different elements. She applied the up-to-date theory of spectral line formation and found that the chemical compositions of stars were probably all similar, with the temperature being the important factor in creating their diverse appearances. She was then able to estimate the abundances of seventeen of the elements relative to the eighteenth, silicon. Hydrogen appeared to be more than a million times more abundant than silicon, a conclusion so unexpected that it took many years to become widely accepted.

In such an analysis of chemical abundances, the wavelength of each line is treated as fixed. However, this is not true when the star is moving toward us (the lines are observed at shorter wavelengths, or "blue-shifted", compared to those measured in the laboratory) or moving away from us (observed at longer wavelengths, or "red-shifted"). This is the phenomenon of "Doppler shift".

If the spectrum of a star is red- or blue-shifted, then you can use that to infer its velocity along the line of sight. Such radial velocity studies have had at least three important applications in astrophysics.

The first is the study of binary star systems. The component stars in a binary revolve around each other. You can measure the radial velocities for one cycle (or more) of the binary, then you can relate that back to the gravitational pull using Newton's equations of motion (or their astrophysical applications, Kepler's laws).

If you have additional information, such as from observations of eclipses, then you can sometimes measure the masses of the stars accurately. Eclipsing binaries, in which you can see the spectral lines of both stars, have played a crucial role in establishing the masses and the radii of different types of stars.

The second is the study of the structure of our galaxy. Stars in the galaxy revolve around its centre, just like planets revolve around the sun. However it is more complicated, because the gravity is due to all the stars in the galaxy combined in this case. In the solar system, the sun is such a dominant source that you can virtually ignore the pull of the planets. So, radial velocity studies of stars (binary or single) have played a major role in establishing the shape of the galaxy. It is still an active field today. For example, one of the evidences for dark matter comes from the study of the distribution of velocities at different distances from the centre of the galaxy. Another recent development is the radial velocity studies of stars very near the galactic centre, which strongly suggest that our galaxy contains a massive black hole.

The third is the expansion of the universe. Edwin Hubble established that more distant galaxies tended to have more red-shifted spectra. Although not predicted even by Einstein, such an expanding universe is a natural solution for his theory of general relativity. Today, for more distant galaxies, the red-shift is used as a primary indicator of their distances. The ratio of the recession velocity to the distance is called the Hubble Constant, and the precise measurement of its value has been one of the major accomplishments of astrophysics today, using such tools as the Hubble Space Telescope.

Quantum mechanics predicts the existence of what are usually called "zero point" energies for the strong, the weak and the electromagnetic interactions, where the "zero point" refers to the energy of the system at temperature $T=0$, or the lowest quantised energy level of a quantum mechanical system. Although the term zero point energy applies to all three of these interactions in nature, customarily (and hereafter in this section) it is used in reference only to the electromagnetic case.

In conventional quantum physics, the origin of zero point energy is the Heisenberg uncertainty principle, which states that, for a moving particle such as an electron, the more precisely one measures the position, the less exact the best possible measurement of its momentum (mass times velocity), and vice versa. The least possible uncertainty of position multiplied by momentum is specified by Planck's constant, h.

A parallel uncertainty exists between measurements involving time and energy (and other so-called conjugate variables in quantum mechanics). This minimum uncertainty is not due to any correctable flaws in measurement, but rather reflects an intrinsic quantum fuzziness in the very nature of energy and matter springing from the wave nature of the various quantum fields. This leads to the concept of zero point energy.

Zero point energy is the energy that remains when all other energy is removed from a system. This behaviour is demonstrated by, for example, liquid helium. As the temperature is lowered to absolute zero, helium remains a liquid, rather than freezing to a solid, owing to the irremovable zero point energy of its atomic motions. (Increasing the pressure to 25 atmospheres will cause helium to freeze.)

A harmonic oscillator is a useful conceptual tool in physics. Classically a harmonic oscillator, such as a mass on a spring, can always be brought to rest. However a quantum harmonic oscillator does not permit this. A residual motion will always remain due to the requirements of the Heisenberg uncertainty principle, resulting in a zero point energy, equal to $1/2\ hf$, where f is the oscillation frequency.

Electromagnetic radiation can be pictured as waves flowing through space at the speed of light. The waves are not waves of anything substantive, but are ripples in a state of a theoretically defined field. However these waves do carry energy (and momentum), and each wave has a specific direction, frequency and polarisation state. Each wave represents a "propagating mode of the electromagnetic field".

Each mode is equivalent to a harmonic oscillator and is thus subject to the Heisenberg uncertainty principle. From this analogy, every mode of the field must have 1/2 *hf* as its average minimum energy. That is a tiny amount of energy in each mode, but the number of modes is enormous, and indeed increases per unit frequency interval as the square of the frequency. The spectral energy density is determined by the density of modes times the energy per mode and per volume, and thus increases as the cube of the frequency per unit volume. The product of the tiny energy per mode times the huge spatial density of modes yields a very high theoretical zero point energy density per cubic centimetre.

From this line of reasoning, quantum physics predicts that all of space must be filled with electromagnetic zero point fluctuations (also called the zero point field) creating a universal sea of zero point energy. The density of this energy depends critically on where in frequency the zero point fluctuations cease. Since space itself is thought to break up into a kind of quantum foam at a tiny distance scale called the Planck length (10^{-33} cm), it is argued that the zero point fluctuations must cease at a corresponding Planck frequency (10^{43} Hz). If that is the case, the zero point energy density would be 110 orders of magnitude greater than the radiant energy at the centre of the sun.

How could such an enormous amount of energy not be wildly evident? There is one major difference between zero point electromagnetic radiation and ordinary electromagnetic radiation. Turning again to the Heisenberg uncertainty principle one finds that the lifetime of a given zero point photon, viewed as a wave, corresponds to an average distance travelled of only a fraction of its wavelength. Such a wave fragment is somewhat different to an ordinary plane wave, and it is difficult to know how to interpret this.

On the other hand, zero point energy appears to have been directly measured as current noise in a resistively shunted Josephson junction by Koch, van Harlingen and Clarke up to a frequency of about 600 GHz.

CHAPTER 22

In this section dealing with scientific advances from 1970 onwards, we will discuss the advances that have had a profound effect on everyone's life. There have been so many huge advances over the last few decades that they would warrant a book in themselves. In this section therefore, we will be discussing primarily the Internet, the GPS system, mobile phones and lasers. For the younger readers, I'm sure that you could not imagine what life was like before these technologies were developed.

I remember my first mobile phone. It was a bulky item which needed to be fitted to a car. The handset alone was far bigger than a modern iPhone, and needed to be connected to a transceiver also fitted within the car. I had this equipment fitted as soon as it was available. At the time, I was often on the way to a meeting with an oil company, when their secretary would phone my secretary, saying that the meeting had to be cancelled due to a more pressing problem that had occurred. My secretary was unable to communicate this information to me, so I would spend maybe one hour driving across Aberdeen in heavy traffic before I discovered that the meeting had been cancelled, only to return back to my office after having wasted two hours of the day.

The Internet has revolutionised the computer and communications world like nothing before. The invention of the telegraph, telephone, radio and computer set the stage for this unprecedented integration of capabilities. The Internet now has a worldwide broadcasting capability, a mechanism for information dissemination, and a medium for collaboration and interaction between individuals and their computers without regard for geographic location. The Internet represents one of the most successful examples of the benefits of sustained investment and commitment to scientific research and development of information infrastructure. Beginning with the early research into packet switching, governments, industry and academia have been partners in evolving and deploying this exciting new technology.

This section of the book is intended to be a brief and incomplete history. Much material currently exists about the Internet, covering history, technology and usage. The history revolves around several distinct aspects.

There is the technological evolution that began with early research on packet switching and the ARPANET (Advanced Research Projects Agency Network), where current research continues to expand the horizons of the infrastructure along several dimensions, such as scale, performance and higher-level functionality.

There is the operations and management aspect of a global and complex operational infrastructure. There is the social aspect, which resulted in a broad community of

"Internauts" working together to create and evolve the technology. Finally there is the commercialisation aspect, resulting in an extremely effective transition of research results into a broadly deployed and available information infrastructure.

The Internet today is a widespread information infrastructure, the initial prototype of what is often called the National (or Global or Galactic) Information Infrastructure. Its history is complex and involves many technological and organisational aspects. Its influence reaches not only to the technical fields of computer communications but throughout society as we move towards the increasing use of online tools to accomplish electronic commerce, information acquisition and community operations.

The first recorded description of the social interactions that could be enabled through networking was in a series of memos written at MIT (Massachusetts Institute of Technology) in August 1962 discussing this "Galactic Network" concept. They envisioned a globally interconnected set of computers through which everyone could quickly access data and programs from any site. In spirit, the concept was very much like the Internet of today. The computer research programme into this concept began at DARPA (Defence Advanced Research Projects Agency), starting in October 1962.

MIT published the first paper on packet switching theory in July 1961 and the first book on the subject in 1964. MIT understood the theoretical feasibility of communications using packets rather than circuits, which was a major step along the path towards computer networking. The other key step was to make the computers talk together. To explore this, in 1965 MIT connected their TX-2 computer to a Q-32 computer in California with a low-speed dial-up telephone line, creating the first (however small) wide-area computer network ever built. The result of this experiment was the realisation that the time-shared computers could work well together, running programs and retrieving data as necessary on the remote machine, but that the circuit switched telephone system was totally inadequate for the job.

In late 1966 MIT went on to develop the computer network concept, and quickly put together a comprehensive plan, publishing it in 1967. The word "packet" was adopted from the work at MIT, and the proposed line speed to be used in the ARPANET design was upgraded from 2.4 kbps to 50 kbps. The network topology and economics were designed and optimised by an engineering team at UCLA (University of California, Los Angeles).

Soon after this the first host-to-host message was sent. Two more nodes were added at UC Santa Barbara and at the University of Utah. These last two nodes incorporated application visualisation projects.

UCSB investigated methods for the display of mathematical functions using storage displays to deal with the problem of refresh over the net, and investigated methods of 3D representations over the net. Thus, by the end of 1969, four host computers were connected together into the initial ARPANET, and the budding Internet was off the ground. Even at this early stage, it should be noted that the networking research incorporated both work on the underlying network and work on how to utilise the network. This tradition continues to this day.

Computers were added quickly to the ARPANET during the following years, and work proceeded on completing a functioning host-to-host protocol and other network software. In December 1970 the Network Working Group (NWG) finished the initial ARPANET host-to-host protocol, called the Network Control Protocol (NCP). As the ARPANET sites completed implementing NCP during the period 1971–72, the network users could finally begin to develop applications.

In October 1972 a large and very successful demonstration of the ARPANET was given at the International Computer Communication Conference (ICCC). This was the first demonstration of this new network technology to the public. It was also in 1972 that the initial "hot" application, electronic mail, was introduced.

In July 1973, engineers further expanded its power by writing the first email utility program that could list, selectively read, file, forward and respond to messages. From there email took off as the largest network application for over a decade. This was the embryo of the kind of activity we see on the World Wide Web today, namely, the enormous growth in all kinds of "people-to-people" traffic.

The original ARPANET grew into the Internet. The Internet was based on the idea that there would be multiple independent networks of rather arbitrary design, beginning with the ARPANET as the pioneering packet switching network. However it was soon to include packet satellite networks, ground-based packet radio networks and other networks.

The Internet as we now know it embodies a key underlying technical idea, namely that of open architecture networking. In this approach, the choice of any individual network technology was not dictated by a particular network architecture but rather could be selected freely by a provider. It could be made to work with the other networks through a multi-level "internetworking architecture".

Up until that time there was only one general method for federating networks. This was the traditional circuit switching method where networks would interconnect at the circuit level. This was achieved by passing individual bits on a synchronous basis along a portion of an end-to-end circuit between a pair of end locations.

While there were other limited ways to interconnect different networks, they required that one be used as a component of the other, rather than acting as a peer of the other in offering end-to-end service. In an open-architecture network, the individual networks may be separately designed and developed and each may have its own unique interface which it may offer to users and/or other providers. Each network can be designed in accordance with the specific environment and user requirements of that network. There are generally no constraints on the types of network that can be included or on their geographic scope, although certain pragmatic considerations will dictate what makes sense to offer.

Key to making the packet radio system work was a reliable end-to-end protocol that could maintain effective communication in the face of jamming and other radio interference, and withstand intermittent blackout such as would be caused by being in a tunnel or blocked by the local terrain. It was first contemplated that developing a protocol local only to the packet radio network would work, since that would avoid having to deal with the multitude of different operating systems, and continuing to use NCP.

However, NCP did not have the ability to address networks (and machines) further downstream than a destination server on the ARPANET, and thus some change to NCP would also be required. (The assumption was that the ARPANET was not changeable in this regard.) NCP relied on ARPANET to provide end-to-end reliability. If any packets were lost, the protocol (and presumably any applications it supported) would come to a grinding halt.

In this model NCP had no end-to-end host error control, since the ARPANET was to be the only network in existence and it would be so reliable that no error control would be required on the part of the hosts. Thus it was decided to develop a new version of the protocol which could meet the needs of an open-architecture network environment. This protocol would eventually be called the Transmission Control Protocol/Internet Protocol (TCP/IP). While NCP tended to act like a device driver, the new protocol would be more like a communications protocol.

Commercialisation of the Internet involved not only the development of competitive, private network services, but also the development of commercial products implementing the Internet technology. In the early 1980s, dozens of vendors were incorporating TCP/IP into their products because they saw buyers for that approach to networking. Unfortunately they lacked both real information about how the technology was supposed to work, and how the customers planned on using this approach to networking. Many saw it as a nuisance add-on that had to be glued on to their own proprietary networking solutions. The US DoD had mandated the use of TCP/IP in many of its purchases, but gave little help to the vendors regarding how to build useful TCP/IP products.

In 1985, recognising this lack of information availability and appropriate training, a three-day workshop was arranged for all vendors to learn about how TCP/IP worked, and what it still could not do well. The speakers came mostly from the research community who had both developed these protocols and used them in day-to-day work. About 250 vendor personnel came to listen to fifty inventors and experimenters. The results were surprising for both sides. The vendors were amazed to find that the inventors were so open about the way things worked (and what still did not work), and the inventors were pleased to listen to new problems they had not considered, but were being discovered by the vendors in the field. Thus a two-way discussion was formed that lasted for over a decade.

After two years of conferences, tutorials, design meetings and workshops, a special event was organised that invited those vendors whose products ran TCP/IP well to come together in one room for three days to show off how well they all worked together over the Internet. In September of 1988 the first Interop trade show was born. Fifty companies made the cut, and 5,000 engineers from potential customer organisations came to see if it all worked as was promised. It did. This was because the vendors worked extremely hard to ensure that everyone's products interoperated with all of the other products, and even with those of their competitors. The Interop trade show has grown immensely since then, and today it is held in seven locations around the world each year. An audience of over 250,000 people come to learn which products work with each other in a seamless manner, to learn about the latest products, and discuss the latest technology.

In parallel with the commercialisation efforts, the vendors began to attend meetings that were held three or four times a year to discuss new ideas for extensions of the

TCP/IP protocol suite. Starting with a few hundred attendees mostly from academia and paid for by the government, these meetings now often exceed a thousand attendees, mostly from the vendor community and paid for by the attendees themselves. The reason it is so useful is that it is composed of all stakeholders, researchers, end users and vendors.

Network management provides an example of the interplay between the research and commercial communities. In the beginning of the Internet, the emphasis was on defining and implementing protocols that achieved interoperation. As the network grew larger, it became clear that the sometimes ad hoc procedures used to manage the network would no longer work. Manual configuration of tables was replaced by distributed automated algorithms, and better tools were devised to isolate faults.

In 1987 it became clear that a protocol was needed that would permit the elements of the network, such as the routers, to be remotely managed in a uniform way. Several protocols for this purpose were proposed, including Simple Network Management Protocol or SNMP (designed, as its name would suggest, for simplicity, and derived from an earlier proposal called SGMP), HEMS (a more complex design from the research community) and CMIP (from the OSI community).

A series of meetings led to the decision that HEMS would be withdrawn as a candidate for standardisation, but that work on both SNMP and CMIP would go forward, with the idea that the SNMP could be a more near-term solution and CMIP a longer-term approach. The market could choose the one it found more suitable. SNMP is now used almost universally for network-based management.

The Internet has changed enormously since it came into existence. It was conceived in the era of time-sharing, but has progressed into the era of personal computers, client-server and peer-to-peer computing, the network computer, smartphones and tablets. It was designed before LANs existed, but has accommodated that network technology, as well as the more recent ATM and frame switched services. It was envisioned as supporting a range of functions from file sharing and remote login to resource sharing and collaboration, and has spawned electronic mail and the World Wide Web. But most importantly, it started as the creation of a small band of dedicated researchers, and has grown to be a commercial success with billions of dollars' worth of annual investment.

One should not conclude that the Internet has now finished changing. The Internet, although a network in name and geography, is a creature of the computer, not the traditional network of the telephone or television industry. It will, and indeed it must, continue to change and evolve at the speed of the computer industry if it is to remain relevant. It is now changing to provide new services such as real time transport, in order to support, for example, audio and video streams.

The availability of pervasive networking (i.e. the Internet) along with powerful, affordable computing and communications in portable form (i.e. laptop computers, smartphones and tablets), is making possible a new paradigm of nomadic computing and communications. This evolution will bring us new applications in the future. It is evolving to permit more sophisticated forms of pricing and cost recovery, a perhaps painful requirement in this commercial world.

New modes of access and new forms of service will spawn new applications, which in turn will drive further evolution of the net itself. The most pressing question for the future of the Internet is not how the technology will change, but how the process of change and evolution itself will be managed. With the success of the Internet has come a proliferation of stakeholders – stakeholders now with an economic as well as an intellectual investment in the network.

We now see, in the debates over control of the domain name space and the form of the next generation IP addresses, a struggle to find the next social structure that will guide the Internet in the future. The form of that structure will be harder to find, given the large number of concerned stakeholders. At the same time, the industry struggles to find the economic rationale for the large investment needed for the future growth, for example to upgrade residential access to a more suitable ultra-fast technology. If the Internet stumbles, it will not be because we lack for technology, vision or motivation. It will be because we cannot set a direction and march collectively into the future.

Now we will turn our attention to the Global Positioning System (GPS). For centuries, navigators and explorers have searched the heavens for a system that would enable them to locate their position on the globe with the accuracy necessary to avoid tragedy and to reach their intended destinations. On 26th June 1993, however, this quest became a reality. On that date, the US Air Force launched the twenty-fourth Navstar satellite into orbit, completing a network of twenty-four satellites known as the Global Positioning System. With a GPS receiver that costs a few hundred dollars, you can instantly find your location on the planet. Your latitude, longitude and even altitude will be known to within a few metres.

This incredible new technology was made possible by a combination of scientific and engineering advances, particularly the development of the world's most accurate time pieces, atomic clocks which are precise to within a billionth of a second. The clocks were created by physicists seeking answers to questions about the nature of the universe, with no conception that their technology would some day lead to a global system of navigation. Today, GPS is saving lives, helping society in countless other ways, and generating thousands of jobs in a multi-billion dollar industry.

In addition, atomic clocks have been used to confirm Einstein's hypothesis that time slows down in the observer's frame of reference as you increase in speed. I remember many years ago that British Airways were loaned two atomic clocks, which they placed at Heathrow airport for a week. This was to confirm that the two clocks registered exactly the same time during this period.

One clock was then placed on a flight from London to Sydney. When the aircraft returned, the time on the two clocks were compared. It was found that the clock that had been aboard the aircraft recorded time more slowly than the clock that was stationary in London. Although the timing difference registered was only billionths of a second, this confirmed an important pillar of Einstein's space time predictions.

When global positioning (GPS) was initially introduced, although it had the technical ability to be fantastically accurate, the American military deliberately corrupted the system using what was known at the time as "selective availability". This meant that some erroneous information was transmitted in order to degrade the accuracy which the system was capable of. US military specification GPS filtered out the selective availability.

I remember when I purchased my first boat, I fitted a GPS system in order that we could have a navigational backup to the conventional systems. Our position jumped around regularly. Even when we were tied up at the quayside, the GPS would move the reported position of our boat by up to 100 metres at regular intervals.

Selective availability was supposedly introduced in order that foreign powers could not use this incredibly accurate system to target their weapons. It is difficult to imagine who thought up this ridiculous scenario. The designers of the system must have thought of including secondary and tertiary systems that they could switch to at the press of a button, which would encrypt the positioning information, making it only available to the US military. No foreign power would be stupid enough to use a guidance system for their weapons over which the Americans had absolute control.

Selective availability was finally switched off when the penny dropped on this point, and also after GPS tracking was incorporated into all mobile smartphones. Using this feature, it enabled the authorities to precisely find the location of any mobile phone. This had huge benefits for the rescue and law enforcement services. We are now able to locate any mobile phone to within a matter of metres, even if it is switched off.

Advances in technology and new demands on the existing system have now led to efforts to modernise the GPS system and implement the next generation of GPS III satellites, and the next generation Operational Control System (OCS). Announcements from the White House initiated these changes, and then the US Congress authorised the modernisation effort to implement GPS III.

In addition to GPS, other systems are in use or under development. The Russian Global Navigation Satellite

System (GLONASS) was developed during the same period as GPS, but suffered from incomplete coverage of the globe until the mid-2000s. There are also the planned European Union Galileo positioning system, the Indian Regional Navigational Satellite System and the Chinese Compass Navigation System.

Restrictions have been placed on the civilian use of GPS. The US government controls the export of some civilian receivers. All GPS receivers capable of functioning at above 18 kilometres (11 miles) in altitude and 515 metres per second, or designed or modified for use with unmanned air vehicles such as ballistic or cruise missile systems and drones, are classified as munitions (weapons) and therefore require State Department export licences.

Previously this rule applied even to otherwise purely civilian units that only received the L1 frequency and the C/A (Coarse/Acquisition) code, and could not correct for selective availability. The US government discontinued SA on 1st May 2000, resulting in a much improved autonomous GPS accuracy.

Disabling operation above these limits exempts the receiver from classification as a munition. Vendor interpretations differ. The rule refers to operation at both the target altitude and speed, but some receivers stop operating even when stationary. This has caused problems with some amateur radio balloon launches that regularly reach altitudes of 30 kilometres (19 miles).

These limitations only apply to units exported from (or which have components exported from) the USA. There is a growing trade in various components, including GPS units, supplied by other countries, which are expressly sold as ITAR free.

CHAPTER 23

Now we will move on to discuss mobile phones. The type of wireless communication that is the most familiar today is the mobile phone. It is often called "cellular" because the system uses many base stations to divide a service area into multiple cells. Cellular calls are transferred from base station to base station as a user travels from cell to cell.

The basic concept of cellular phones began in 1947, when researchers looked at crude mobile car phones and realised that by using small cells they could substantially increase the range and traffic capacity of mobile phones. However at that time, the technology to do so did not exist.

Anything to do with broadcasting and sending a radio or television message out over the airwaves comes under government regulation. A cell phone is a type of two-way radio. In the 1950s, various companies proposed that the authorities should allocate a large number of radio frequencies so that a widespread mobile telephone service would become feasible. They would then also have an incentive to research the new technology required. We can partially blame the government departments for the gap between the initial concept of a cellular service and its availability to the public.

Initially very few frequency bands were approved. The government reconsidered its position in 1968, stating, "If the technology to build a better mobile service works, we will increase the frequency allocation, freeing the airwaves for more mobile phones." Prospective system operators then proposed a cellular network of many small, low-powered broadcast towers, each covering a cell of a few miles in radius but collectively covering a much larger area. Each tower would use only a few of the total frequencies allocated to the system. As the phones travelled across the area, calls would be passed from tower to tower.

The first fully automated mobile phone system for vehicles was launched in Sweden in 1956. Named MTA (Mobiltelefonisystem A), it allowed calls to be made and received in the car using a rotary dial. The car phone could also be paged. Calls from the car were direct-dial, whereas incoming calls required an operator to determine which base station the phone was currently at. It was developed by Sture Lauren and other engineers at Televerket network operator.

Ericsson provided the switchboard while Svenska Radioaktiebolaget (SRA) and Marconi provided the telephones and base station equipment. MTA phones consisted of vacuum tubes and relays, and weighed 40 kg. In 1962, an upgraded version called Mobile Telephone B

(MTB) was introduced. This was a push-button telephone, and used transistors and DTMF signalling to improve its operational reliability. In 1971 the MTD version was launched, and by that time several different brands of equipment were gaining commercial success. The network remained open until 1983, and had 600 customers when it closed.

ANALOGUE CELLULAR NETWORKS (1G)

The first automatic analogue cellular systems deployed were NTT's system, first used in Tokyo in 1979. This system later spread to the whole of Japan, and NTT was first used in the Nordic countries in 1981.

The first analogue cellular system widely deployed in North America was the Advanced Mobile Phone System (AMPS). It was commercially introduced in the Americas in October 1983, Israel in 1986 and Australia in 1987. AMPS was a pioneering technology that helped drive the mass market usage of cellular technology, but it had several serious issues by modern standards. Firstly it was unencrypted, and easily vulnerable to eavesdropping via a scanner. It was also susceptible to cell phone cloning, and it used a Frequency Division Multiple Access (FDMA) system that required significant amounts of the available wireless frequency spectrum to support it.

On 6th March 1983, Dyna TAC Mobile Phone launched the first US 1G network. It cost $100 million to develop, and took over a decade to reach the market. The phone had a talk time of just half an hour, and took ten hours to recharge. Consumer demand was strong despite the battery life, weight and low talk time, and waiting lists were in the thousands.

Many of the iconic early commercial cell phones such as the Motorola Dyna TAC Analogue AMPS were eventually superseded by Digital AMPS (D-AMPS) in 1990, and the AMPS service was shut down by most North American carriers by 2008.

DIGITAL CELLULAR NETWORKS (2G)

In the 1990s, the second-generation mobile phone systems emerged. Two systems competed for supremacy in the global market. They were the European-developed GSM standard and the US-developed CDMA standard. These differed from the previous generation by using digital instead of analogue transmission, and also fast out-of-band phone-to-network signalling. The rise in mobile phone usage as a result of 2G was explosive, and this era also saw the advent of prepaid mobile phones.

In 1991 the first GSM network (Radiolinja) was launched in Finland. In general the frequencies used by 2G systems in Europe were higher than those in America, though with some overlap. For example, the 900 MHz frequency range was used for both 1G and 2G systems in Europe; so the 1G systems were rapidly closed down to make space for the 2G systems. In America the IS-54 standard was deployed in the same band as AMPS, and displaced some of the existing analogue channels.

In 1993, the IBM Simon was introduced. This was possibly the world's first smartphone. It was a mobile phone, pager, fax machine and PDA all rolled into one. It included a calendar, address book, clock, calculator, notepad, email and a touchscreen with a QWERTY keyboard. The IBM Simon had a stylus you used to tap the touchscreen with. It featured predictive typing that would guess the next characters as you tapped. It had applications, or at least a way to deliver more features by plugging a PCMCIA 1.8 MB memory card into the phone.

Coinciding with the introduction of 2G systems was a trend away from the larger brick-sized phones toward tiny 100–200 gram handheld devices. This change was possible not only through technological improvements such as more advanced batteries and more energy-efficient electronics, but also because of the higher density of cell sites to accommodate increasing usage. The latter meant that the average distance transmission from phone to the base station shortened, leading to increased battery life whilst on the move.

The second generation introduced a new variant of communication called SMS or text messaging. It was initially available only on GSM networks but spread eventually to all digital networks. The first machine-generated SMS message was sent in the UK on 3rd

December 1992, followed in 1993 by the first person-to-person SMS sent in Finland. The advent of prepaid services in the late 1990s soon made SMS the communication method of choice amongst the young, a trend which then spread across all age groups.

2G also introduced the ability to access media content on mobile phones. In 1998 the first downloadable content sold to mobile phones was the ringtone, launched by Finland's Radiolinja (now Elisa). Advertising on the mobile phone first appeared in Finland when a free daily SMS news headline service was launched in 2000, sponsored by advertising.

Mobile payments were trialled in 1998 in Finland and Sweden, where a mobile phone was used to pay for a Coca-Cola vending machine and car parking. Commercial launches followed in 1999 in Norway. The first commercial payment system to mimic banks and credit cards was launched in the Philippines in 1999, simultaneously by mobile operators Globe and Smart.

The first full Internet service on mobile phones was introduced by NTT DoCoMo in Japan in 1999.

MOBILE BROADBAND DATA (3G)

As the use of 2G phones became more widespread and people began to utilise mobile phones in their daily lives, it became clear that demand for data (such as access to browse the Internet) was growing. Further experience from fixed broadband services showed there would also be an ever-increasing demand for greater data speeds. The 2G technology was nowhere near up to the job, so the industry began to work on the next generation of technology known as 3G. The main technological difference that distinguishes 3G technology from 2G technology is the use of packet switching rather than circuit switching for data transmission. In addition, the standardisation process focused on requirements more than technology (2 Mbs maximum data rate indoors and 384 Kbs outdoors, for example).

Inevitably this led to many competing standards with different contenders pushing their own technologies, and the vision of a single unified worldwide standard looked far from reality. The standard 2G CDMA networks became 3G compliant with the adoption of Revision A to EV-DO, which made several additions to the protocol while retaining backwards compatibility.

The first network with 3G was launched by NTT DoCoMo in the Tokyo region of Japan in May 2001. European launches of 3G were made soon after in Italy and the UK by the Three/Hutchison group. The high connection speeds of 3G technology enabled a transformation in the industry. For the first time, media streaming of radio and television content to 3G handsets became possible, with companies such as Real Networks and Disney among the early pioneers in this type of offering.

In the mid-2000s, an evolution of 3G technology began to be implemented, namely High Speed Downlink Packet Access (HSDPA). It is an enhanced 3G mobile telephony communications protocol in the High Speed Packet Access (HSPA) family, also coined 3.5G, 3G+ or turbo 3G. It allows networks based on Universal Mobile Telecommunications System (UMTS) to have higher data transfer speeds and capacity. Current HSDPA deployments support downlink speeds of 1.8, 3.6, 7.2 and 14.0 Mbs.

By the end of 2013, there were 1.28 billion subscribers on 3G networks worldwide. The 3G telecoms services generated over $220 billion of revenue during 2013 and in many markets the majority of new phones activated were 3G phones. In Japan and South Korea the market no longer supplies phones of the second generation.

Although mobile phones had long had the ability to access data networks such as the Internet, it was not until the widespread availability of good quality 3G coverage in the mid-2000s that specialised devices appeared to access the mobile Internet. The first such devices, known as "dongles", plugged directly into a computer through the USB port. Another new class of device appeared subsequently, the so-called "compact wireless router" such as the Novatel MiFi. These made the existing 3G Internet connectivity available to multiple computers simultaneously over Wi-Fi, rather than just to a single computer via a USB plug-in.

Such devices became especially popular for use with laptop computers due to the added portability they bestow. Consequently, some computer manufacturers started to embed the mobile data function directly into the laptop so a dongle or MiFi wasn't needed. Instead, the SIM card could be inserted directly into the device itself to access the mobile data services. Such 3G-capable laptops became commonly known as "netbooks". Other types of data-aware devices followed in the netbook's footsteps. By the beginning of 2010, e-readers, such as the Amazon Kindle and the Nook from Barnes & Noble, had already become available with embedded wireless Internet, and Apple had announced plans for embedded wireless Internet on its iPad tablet devices beginning in late 2010.

NATIVE IP NETWORKS (4G)

By 2009, it had become clear that, at some point, 3G networks would be overwhelmed by the growth of bandwidth-intensive applications like streaming media. Consequently, the industry began looking to data-optimised fourth-generation technologies, with the promise of speed improvements up to tenfold over existing 3G technologies. The first two commercially available technologies billed as 4G were the WiMAX standard (offered in the US by Sprint) and the LTE standard, first offered in Scandinavia by TeliaSonera.

One of the main ways in which 4G differed technologically from 3G was in its elimination of circuit switching, instead employing an all-IP network. Thus, 4G ushered in a treatment of voice calls just like any other type of streaming audio media, utilising packet switching over Internet, LAN or WAN networks. As we head towards 2020, the second half of this decade will certainly see the widespread introduction of 4G infrastructure, and further technical advances will be in the pipeline.

LASERS

The final major scientific and technological advance of this era that has had a profound effect on everyone's life was the development of the laser. Lasers can burn movies onto DVDs, mark diamonds, precision cut metals, destroy missiles, perform eye surgery, cancer surgery and cosmetic surgery, and they can even whiten teeth.

Natural light, or sunlight, contains an entire spectrum of frequencies with which we are all familiar. In the early days of science, monochromatic light could be produced using sodium lamps and other devices. However, although the light was monochromatic, that is of a single specific frequency, it was not coherent. That means that the photons in the light emitted were not in phase. The unique feature of laser light is that it is not only monochromatic, but it is also coherent, which gives it some special and very useful properties.

I became interested in lasers when I was still at school. I remember saving the money that I earned from my paper round and eventually buying my first laser. It was manufactured by a company called Melles Griot and was a helium neon laser. It had a power of 2 mW and produced a beam of red laser light at a wavelength of 632.8 nm.

Unlike in James Bond movies, you cannot see the path of a "visible wavelength" laser beam in clean air. The beam is only visible if the air contains dust particles or smoke which will reflect some of the light, thereby revealing its path. In addition, lasers do not make silly noises when they operate.

The device itself was around 20cm long, but it also required a power pack of about the same size. At that time, solid-state lasers had not been developed. The early lasers such as mine consisted of an evacuated glass plasma tube containing the necessary components to enable the device to operate. Subsequently, glass tube lasers were replaced by solid-state lasers, in exactly the same way that transistors and microchips replaced the valves (tubes). Today solid-state lasers are produced that operate both within and outside the visible light spectrum.

The word laser is the acronym for Light Amplification by Stimulated Emission of Radiation. Albert Einstein first explained the theory of stimulated emission in 1917, which became the basis of laser. He postulated that, when the population inversion exists between upper and lower levels among atomic systems, it is possible to realise amplified stimulated emission, and the stimulated emission would have the same frequency and phase as the incident radiation. However, it was in late the 1940s and 1950s that scientists and engineers did extensive work to realise a practical device based on the principle of stimulated emission. Notable scientists who pioneered the work include Charles Townes, Joseph Weber, Alexander Prokhorov and Nikolai G Basov.

Initially, the scientists and engineers were working towards the realisation of a MASER (Microwave Amplification by the Stimulated Emission of Radiation), a device that amplified microwaves for its immediate application in microwave communication systems. Townes and the other engineers believed it to be possible to create an optical maser, a device for creating powerful beams of light using higher frequency energy to stimulate what was to be termed the lasing medium. Despite the pioneering work of Townes and Prokhorov it was left to Theodore Maiman in 1960 to invent the first laser using ruby as a lasing medium that was stimulated using high-energy flashes of intense light.

The development of lasers has been a turning point in the history of science and engineering. It has produced completely new types of systems with the potential for applications in a wide variety of fields. During the 1960s, a lot of work had been carried out on the basic development of almost all the major lasers including high-power gas dynamic and chemical lasers. Almost all the practical applications of these lasers in defence as well as in industry were also identified during this period. The motivation of using the high-power lasers in a strategic scenario was a great driving force for the rapid development of these high-power lasers. In early 1970s, megawatt class carbon dioxide gas dynamic lasers were successfully developed and tested against typical military targets. The development of chemical lasers, free electron and X-ray lasers took a slightly longer time because of involvement of a multidisciplinary approach.

Chemical lasers are powered by a chemical reaction permitting a large amount of energy to be released quickly. Such very high-power lasers are especially of interest to the military. However continuous wave chemical lasers at very high-power levels fed by streams of gases have been developed, and have some industrial applications. As examples, in the hydrogen fluoride laser (2,700–2,900 nm) and the deuterium fluoride laser (3,800 nm), the reaction is the combination of hydrogen or deuterium gas with combustion products of ethylene in nitrogen trifluoride.

Excimer lasers are a special sort of gas laser powered by an electric discharge in which the lasing medium is an excimer, or more precisely an exciplex in existing designs. These are molecules which can only exist with one atom in an excited electronic state. Once the molecule transfers its excitation energy to a photon, therefore, its atoms are no longer bound to each other and the molecule disintegrates. This drastically reduces the population of the lower-energy states, thus greatly facilitating a population inversion.

Excimers currently use noble gas compounds. Noble gases are chemically inert and can only form compounds while in an excited state. Excimer lasers typically operate at ultraviolet wavelengths, with major applications including semi-conductor photolithography and LASIK eye surgery. Commonly used excimer molecules include ArF (emission at 193 nm), KrCl (222 nm), KrF (248 nm), XeCl (308 nm) and XeF (351 nm). The molecular fluorine laser, emitting at 157 nm in the vacuum ultraviolet, is sometimes referred to as an excimer laser, however this appears to be a misnomer inasmuch as F_2 is a stable compound.

Solid-state lasers use a crystalline or glass rod which is "doped" with ions that provide the required energy states. For example, the first working laser was made from a ruby crystal (chromium-doped corundum). The population inversion is actually maintained in the "dopant", such as chromium or neodymium. These materials are pumped optically using a shorter wavelength than the lasing wavelength, often from a flashtube or from another laser.

It should be noted that "solid state" in this sense refers to a crystal or glass, but this usage is distinct from the designation of "solid-state electronics" in referring to semiconductors. Semiconductor lasers (laser diodes) are pumped electrically and are thus not referred to as solid-state lasers. The class of solid-state lasers would, however, properly include fibre lasers in which dopants in the glass lase under optical pumping. But in practice these are simply referred to as "fibre lasers", with "solid-state" reserved for lasers using a solid rod of such a material.

Neodymium is a common dopant in various solid-state laser crystals, including yttrium orthovanadate (Nd:YVO$_4$), yttrium lithium fluoride (Nd:YLF) and yttrium aluminium garnet (Nd:YAG). All these lasers can produce high powers in the infrared spectrum at 1064 nm. They are used for cutting, welding and marking of metals and other materials, and also in spectroscopy and for pumping dye lasers.

These lasers are also commonly frequency doubled, tripled or quadrupled, in so-called "diode-pumped solid-state" (DPSS) lasers. Under second, third, or fourth harmonic generation these produce 532 nm (green, visible), 355 nm and 266 nm (UV) beams. This is the technology behind the bright laser pointers, particularly at green (532 nm) and other short visible wavelengths.

Ytterbium, holmium, thulium and erbium are other common dopants in solid-state lasers. Ytterbium is used in crystals such as Yb:YAG, Yb:KGW, Yb:KYW, Yb:SYS, Yb:BOYS and Yb:CaF$_2$, typically operating around 1020–1050 nm. They are potentially very efficient and high-powered due to a small quantum defect. Extremely high-powered ultra-short pulses can be achieved with Yb:YAG. Holmium-doped YAG crystals emitting at 2097 nm form an efficient laser operating at infrared wavelengths strongly absorbed by water-bearing tissues. The Ho-YAG is usually operated in a pulsed mode, and passed through optical fibre surgical devices to resurface joints, remove rot from teeth, vaporise cancers and pulverise kidney and gall stones.

Titanium-doped sapphire (Ti:sapphire) produces a highly tuneable infrared laser, commonly used for spectroscopy. It is also notable for use as a mode-locked laser producing ultra-short pulses of extremely high-peak power.

Thermal limitations in solid-state lasers arise from unconverted pump power that manifests itself as heat. This heat, when coupled with a high thermo-optic coefficient, can give rise to thermal lensing as well as reduced quantum efficiency. These types of issues can be overcome by another novel diode-pumped solid-state laser, the diode-pumped thin disk laser. The thermal limitations in this laser type are mitigated by using a laser medium geometry in which the thickness is much smaller than the diameter of the pump beam. This allows for a more even thermal gradient in the material. Thin disk lasers have been shown to produce up to kilowatt levels of power.

In September 2007, BBC News reported that there was speculation about the possibility of using positron annihilation to drive a very powerful gamma ray laser. Dr David Cassidy of the University of California proposed that a single such laser could be used to ignite a nuclear fusion reaction, replacing the banks of hundreds of lasers currently employed in inertial confinement fusion experiments. Space-based X-ray lasers pumped by a nuclear explosion have also been proposed as antimissile weapons. Such devices would only be one-shot weapons.

Living cells have been used to produce laser light. The cells were genetically engineered to produce green fluorescent protein (GFP). The GFP is used as the laser's "gain medium", where light amplification takes place. The cells were then placed between two tiny mirrors, just 20 millionths of a metre across, which acted as the "laser cavity" in which light could bounce many times through the cells. Upon bathing the cells with blue light, it could be seen to emit directed and intense green laser light.

CHAPTER 24

In this, the penultimate chapter of the book, I will discuss my initial experiences in the business world, and the reasons why I was prompted to head off in my own direction and start my own company in 1984 in order to pursue my fascination with science and technology.

Soon after leaving university, and completing my practical training in the oil and gas industry, my first assignment was with a major oil service company in Abu Dhabi. After two or three trips offshore working as a trainee, I was reassigned to North Gulf division, to work on an ongoing well intervention programme in Basra, southern Iraq. This was at the beginning of 1980, and I was still working in Basra when the first Gulf War started.

The first Gulf War was initiated when Iraqi dictator Saddam Hussein decided to invade Iran. At that time, the Shah of Iran was still in power, and the country was still in favour with the United States. Within days of the war starting, my colleagues and I were minding our own business in the desert, when a group of warplanes appeared. We thought that they would be overflying our position on the way to a military target.

It turned out that they were American-built F-4 Phantoms of the Iranian air force. They came in on a strafing run in an attempt to destroy some of the Iraqi oil-producing infrastructure. I had never been shot at before, but to be strafed with rocket fire from a warplane is terrifying. We just scattered, and following the raid several of my work colleagues had been badly injured and two were dead.

The same day, my surviving colleagues and I decided that enough was enough and we would get out of Iraq. We therefore fuelled up all of our trucks, took all the food and water that we had and drove west towards Saudi Arabia. It took us nearly two days to reach the border, but the Saudis were very generous, yet again, and allowed us to freely enter their country as they knew that Iraq was now a war zone. I spoke to a friend after the Shah fell and the Islamic radicals took power. He jokingly said that the main difference now was that people must pray outside and drink inside.

The Saudis have been very courteous and helpful to me on many occasions, and the only time that I can remember having a problem with a Saudi national was later, when I was working in Dhahran, which I now describe.

The main thing that I sometimes find hard to deal with is some of the hypocrisy that you encounter when travelling, not only overseas but within the UK as well. I remember one particular occasion when I was working for Saudi Aramco in Dhahran. My boss at the time would regularly lecture me on the corruption and decadence in my country. He would also call me an infidel, which is fairly insulting in itself.

After putting up with this all week, my colleagues and I often drove to Bahrain at the weekend, as Bahrain has a very Western-friendly and liberal regime. Bahrain is only a small island, but is a separate sovereign state connected to Saudi Arabia by a causeway. At the weekends, the causeway traffic is horrendous due to Saudis driving to Bahrain in their droves for some rest and recreation.

One weekend we were in a nightclub in one of the major hotels in Bahrain. Astonishingly, I met my boss there. He had a large whisky in one hand and a Filipino hooker in the other. I was utterly shocked by his breath-taking hypocrisy, as I knew that after the weekend he would be back on his ivory tower preaching morality to me yet again.

I believe that the acid test of any religion is its ability to accept, or at least tolerate, tongue-in-cheek commentary regarding their particular faith. It seems to me that many religions are very good at dishing out criticism, but are completely unable to accept any criticism of their own faith.

For example, one of the most hilarious films that I have ever seen was called *The Life of Brian*, produced by Monty Python. It was a total spoof on Christianity and Jesus Christ himself, but it was not banned, and was basically just ignored by the church. Should this type of film be made about some other religions, the perpetrators would have a death sentence placed upon them by the religious fanatics, and would have to go into hiding in fear for their lives.

Anyway, following that aside, we will return to the activities occurring in North Gulf division in 1980. On arriving in Saudi Arabia, I first telephoned my boss to inform him of the situation and where we were. He said that we had done well to save the company's equipment from further destruction and that he would arrange to fly us back to Abu Dhabi.

In fact, he had just hatched a plan to use this situation for his benefit. He knew that the bean counters (aka accounts staff) in Abu Dhabi would never go into a war zone to make an asset inventory. He therefore flew up to Saudi Arabia, in order to debrief us and assess the situation. We then flew down to Abu Dhabi, while he remained in Saudi Arabia.

It subsequently transpired that he arranged for all of the remaining equipment in Basra and other areas in Iraq to be driven into Saudi Arabia, allegedly to protect the company's assets. We later discovered, after he had resigned from the company, that all of this equipment had been sold to another service company operating in the kingdom, and the money he obtained was his nest egg to start his own business. I subsequently learned that he had been on the make previously. When we needed more pickup trucks, we were delivered old used vehicles, but the bean counters in Abu Dhabi told me that the company was invoiced for new vehicles.

The gentleman in question subsequently returned to Aberdeen and started his own business in the fair trade city. Shortly thereafter he became a multi-millionaire from his business activities, but his success was short-lived. He was forced to leave the UK after the initiation of an Inland Revenue investigation. The last time I heard, he was living in South America, and should he ever return to the UK or Europe, the Inland Revenue would very much like to speak to him.

I continued working in the Persian Gulf region for another four years, however I was becoming more and more disillusioned with the business activities of my peers. The final straw came in 1984, when I was told that I would be relocated to Libya.

At that time, Colonel Gaddafi was on the blacklist of most Western powers, as he had already been caught selling Semtex and arms to the IRA, and was suspected of developing his own nuclear programme. At the time of my pending transfer, I had a good Indian friend called Vishnu who had been working for another company in Libya for several years.

When I contacted him he told me not to come. At the time, the Americans had a carrier group in the Gulf of Sidra and had lured the best pilots from the Libyan air force into combat by initiating provocative moves within Libyan airspace. The American warplanes promptly shot down all of the best pilots and aircraft in the Libyan air force, in order to give the US air supremacy over Libya. As soon as this was achieved, the remainder of the Libyan air force was destroyed on the ground. F-111 bombers were then dispatched from American air force bases in the UK, in order to destroy strategic targets within Libya.

Vishnu told me that all he could do was sit in his hotel in Tripoli, watch the bombs fall around him and hope for the best. There were several Americans holed up in the same hotel as him at the time. They told him that they really liked the Brits, as the Americans called our country the *USS UK*, the largest aircraft carrier that they had. They also said that it was the only unsinkable aircraft carrier that they "owned". Nice.

I therefore quit my job in the Middle East and returned to the UK to start my own company. The company did well for many years, as I have related in previous chapters. However in 1995, the international price for crude oil dropped below $10 per barrel. Today this would be unthinkable, but at that time the lifting costs on many fields in the North Sea were above this level.

I think what upsets a lot of Brits is that every time the Americans say, "Jump," the British government says, "How high?" I think the reason for this is that virtually all of the top government officials and civil servants are ex-Eton and Oxbridge, and they do not live in the real world. One hundred years ago Britain was a superpower. Today, although Britain is a great and important country and economic power, we are certainly not a superpower.

I think that most top government officials insist on Britain having a nuclear deterrent, in the belief that the country will be perceived as sitting at the top table in the world power structure. We can no longer afford to develop our own credible independent nuclear deterrent, and the Americans know this. In order to continue sitting at the top table, we need to buy their latest Trident submarine-launched systems, and the government seems prepared to do almost anything in order to keep this system.

I think this attitude was originally ingrained upon politicians when the United Nations was set up. The Security Council only has five permanent members: the United States, Russia, the UK, France and China. These five countries, as the reader will know, were the first five nations to develop nuclear weapons. In a wholly undemocratic system, any one of these five permanent members can veto anything within the Security Council, thereby rendering any proposed resolutions dead in the water should they choose to do so.

I remember one day in 1995 when I was called to a meeting with the contracts department at BP in Aberdeen. They informed me that due to the collapse in the oil price, hundreds of redundancies would be made in their company. Two thirds of the personnel in the contracts department would be laid off, and I was informed that from now on all of the business for BP on the UK continental shelf would be split up into tenders for only three major groups. These would be the northern, central and southern North Sea.

Although my company had been performing successful work for BP for many years, and had a very good track record, it would be very difficult for me to continue under this new system.

When tendering for work, the tender documents are initially provided in two stages. Firstly, they issued the technical tender, in which you are required to prequalify for the commercial phase by demonstrating your technical abilities. Following this, the commercial tender is issued to the technically approved companies. Unfortunately for us, despite our track record, the size of the contracts to be awarded (covering entire swathes of the North Sea per contract), meant that we were effectively excluded from obtaining any further work.

The reason is that the bean counters would reject our commercial tender on the grounds that the financial gearing ratio was way outside the limit of what they were allowed to accept. The problem was that, despite your track record, no company would award you a contract that was worth over half of the entire turnover of your company.

I could see the writing on the wall, and therefore looked to find a far larger company to purchase my own business, so that future tenders would be issued through an organisation large enough to overcome this gearing ratio hurdle. I had no other choice, because if I did nothing I knew that it would be almost impossible to obtain any new contracts, and I would probably be handing out redundancy notices to all of my staff the following year.

I found a company called Scotoil Services that was large enough to absorb my company. Due to our track record and profitability, we negotiated a takeover, whereby they purchased the entire stock of my company and guaranteed to keep all of the staff for at least a two-year period. I was required to resign as the CEO, but was kept on as the business manager in order to oversee the future development of the company.

This initially worked well, and we won a number of new contracts in the North Sea. Some of the new contracts were in the Persian Gulf, as I had many contacts and knowledge of the business in that area. Although I was no longer the CEO of the company, and needed to request permission for each of my business trips, I was treated well and pretty much got what I asked for provided that the bottom line was healthy.

As we had won new contracts in the UAE, on a subsequent business trip my wife asked if she could accompany me. My boss kindly agreed, and the trip went ahead.

During this period, when I returned to Scotland I would tell my wife about my experiences while I had been away. She was born and raised in Stavanger, Norway, and at the time had never travelled outside of Western Europe. Sometimes, after hearing about my overseas trips, she accused me of turning into a racist which I was not happy about, as I have always tried to be courteous and respectful to people of all colours, creeds and religions.

Two weeks later I was due to travel back to Abu Dhabi, and as it was the school holidays her mother came over from Norway to look after the children so that my wife could accompany me on the trip. My client at the time knew that she was coming, as his company made the hotel reservations for our visit. On our first evening in Abu Dhabi, he offered to take us out for a meal.

That evening, the only parking spaces available were two blocks away, so we had about a ten-minute walk to the restaurant. He brought four wives with him, all of whom were completely covered in the normal black dress apart from a small slit for their eyes. My client carried a bamboo cane and every time that we needed to cross the road or change direction, he would strike one of his wives on the side with the cane, in the same way that you herd sheep.

My wife was so outraged by this that I had to physically restrain her or she would have broken his nose. I told her that should she do this, I would lose my contract and she would go to jail, so it was not a good idea. Following this encounter she has never called me racist again.

The problem was that she had absolutely no experience of any culture outside Europe at that time. I told her that rather than attacking the Muslims, she should maybe have a look at the Mormons living around Salt Lake City. Many of them have more wives than wealthy Muslims, and although she may not agree with the behaviour of either group, the world is a diverse place and you must live and let live.

Soon after this, my boss in Scotland sadly died of a heart attack. I was very surprised as he did not smoke or drink, ate healthy food and was a very keen cyclist. One day out of the blue he just collapsed while cycling with friends on the outskirts of Aberdeen. Following this things were very difficult at work, as his children now had control of his company.

I was told by long-term staff members that none of his children had much business acumen or knowledge of the company's operations. However, as the company owned a large city centre site, the plan was to relocate the existing business, sell the land and cash in the chips. This is what eventually happened. The company occupied a 22 acre Brownfield site ideally located adjacent to Aberdeen harbour and the city centre. Most of this site was then sold for commercial development. Today, this site has been developed into a large shopping mall, cinema complex and fast food outlets. I am very sad about this, as these kind of operations do not generate new overseas revenue for the UK economy as we used to do. They just try to take a slice of the existing pie, which is not in the long-term future interests of the UK.

During this period of cost-cutting in the North Sea, there were other complications which caused difficulties for our operations. Shell, for example, virtually closed down the lower levels of its accounting department, outsourcing all of these activities to a local accounting company. I am convinced that the outsourced bean counters were paid bonuses for delaying the payment of approved invoices.

At one stage, we had well in excess of $100,000 in approved yet unpaid invoices to Shell that were with this outsourcing firm awaiting payment. Some of our aged receivables on this list were in excess of ninety days overdue. Every week I would contact the accounting company regarding this and was given excuse after excuse. I was almost miming them to myself as this young man probably read them directly from his standard issue excuses list.

They included, "We have a software fault in the system which we are trying to rectify", "My supervisor is not available to sign the cheques as he is on vacation", and the classic "The cheque was released last week and must be lost in the post. I will cancel it in seven days and then issue a new one." The list went on. I finally ran out of patience and told him that I would contact Shell directly if they did not deliver a cheque to my office within forty-eight hours. He tried to call my bluff.

I went to meet the group leader with Shell and explained the situation. The majority of these invoices were related to pioneering work we had performed using radioactive materials to detect and isolate leaks in the seabed oil storage cells of the Brent Bravo production platform. The success of this operation prevented the shutdown of the biggest UK oilfield, which would have been extremely costly to both Shell and the UK Inland Revenue. The Brent field is so significant that "Brent light" is a worldwide benchmark for crude oil prices. The entire technical staff at Shell were very pleased with our work.

My thoughts were obviously relayed to the accounting company, as I had a cheque in my hand for all the outstanding invoices the following day. However a few weeks later when I needed to visit the accounting company on another matter, I was summoned into a meeting with the young man who handled my account and his boss. The young man was so angry that his face was red and he was physically shaking.

He started to attempt to give me a dressing-down on how unprofessionally I had behaved. After a minute or so, I told him in front of his boss that he had stalled and lied to me again and again, and any unprofessional behaviour was on his side not mine. I also informed the pair of them that should this situation arise again in the future, the same thing would happen. That could well result in adverse consequences for both their company and the individuals who conduct themselves in this manner. I had no more problems with them after this, but it is a shame when people believe that they can get away with this type of behaviour.

Following the sale of the Scotoil city centre site, we were all now looking for new jobs. Due to my experience in the handling of radioactive materials, and my knowledge of the waste disposal regulations in most countries, I was appointed as the technical director of a local company involved in waste management. They wanted to expand their business into radioactive waste management. In the North Sea, most of the radioactive waste is produced as a result of a scale known as NORM (Naturally Occurring Radioactive Material). This forms in oil reservoirs over millions of years, if the rock matrix within the reservoir originally contained any uranium or thorium.

When reservoirs containing these materials are produced, the temperature of the fluids is reduced, causing the dissolved minerals in the already saturated fluid to plate out as solids. This causes low-level radioactive sulphates to be deposited onto everything that the fluid contacts.

This scale material needs to be chipped away or blasted from the pipework, pumps etc., with which they come into contact. The resulting low-level waste was then just dumped into the North Sea. Due to the size of the North Sea, this was not a significant hazard in itself, but it was still a very unsatisfactory way of dealing with waste disposal when there are completely safe and environmentally friendly alternatives should the oil companies choose to use them.

Our initial plan was to containerise this waste and ship it to a controlled site in Aberdeen. We then intended to encapsulate the material in molten glass, which would stabilise it and prevent it from leaching into the environment for thousands of years. Glass is very useful for this purpose. Even today, ancient wrecks are being discovered in the Mediterranean dating back to the days of the ancient Egyptians and Romans. Many of the vessels contain liquids stored in glass bottles, which have remained unbroken and sealed for millennia.

This could have been a major PR coup for some of the oil companies, especially Shell who were still licking their wounds after the Brent Spar PR fiasco. This occurred when they decommissioned a floating oil-loading platform filled with low-level radioactive sludge. They were in the process of towing it out into the North Atlantic to sink it, when the story hit the news. There was such outrage in Europe that Shell were forced to abandon this disposal route, and needed to work very hard to rebuild their environmental reputation.

The problem we encountered with our glass encapsulation proposal was that most of the decision-makers at the top of the oil companies were fairly elderly gentleman close to their retirement. Although they fully appreciated the environmental benefits of the system we were proposing, they did not want to rock the boat by introducing new techniques, and would rather go with the flow for a few more years and retire on a two-thirds final salary package.

The board of my own company considered that this was such a good opportunity that they insisted on patenting the process. I was sceptical about this, as I have had some bitter experiences with patents before. When I ran my own business, I designed various new tools and equipment that were extremely successful. Although I patented these ideas and the equipment developed from them, I knew that unless you had the money to pay a High Court Queen's Counsel (circa $10,000 per day) to fight a patent infringement suit, your patent was effectively worthless.

This had happened to me before when a major oil service company saw my equipment in operation offshore, and they soon made a direct copy of it in blatant breach of my patents. When my solicitor contacted them regarding this, they promptly held an internal meeting. Their assistant district manager at the time rented a home from me in Aberdeen, and was therefore good enough to relay the results of the meeting back to me. He said that the final outcome was that the general manager authorised the release of $800,000 to their legal department, with the instructions "bury the little bastard".

CHAPTER 25

In this final chapter, we will look at three mysterious lakes that are significant due to the modern scientific investigations that have taken place within their waters. These lakes are Loch Ness, Lake Toplitz, and in particular the extraordinary events and NSA involvement surrounding Lake Vostok in Antarctica.

Firstly, Loch Ness. Scotland is both geographically and geologically split into four main sections, due to three large faults crossing the country in a south-west to north-east direction. These faults are the Southern Upland Fault, the Highland Boundary Fault and the Great Glen Fault. The two most southerly of these three faults, the Southern Upland and Highland Boundary, only have one or two small lakes and rivers along their course, but otherwise are not flooded.

The Great Glen Fault, however, was affected by significant glacial erosion during the last Ice Age, and now virtually cuts Scotland in half with a series of lochs (lakes). The largest and most famous of these lakes is Loch Ness. This loch system is connected to the sea on either side of Scotland by the Caledonian Canal.

When my children were younger, we used to take my boat around the north-east of Scotland and enter Loch Ness via the Caledonian Canal. We kept the boat on Loch Ness for the summer, as when the weather there is good it is great for the kids to picnic, play and visit attractions such as the ancient Urquhart Castle on the north-west shore of the loch.

I remember when I was a small boy, my Grandma Lottie used to tell me that Loch Ness was bottomless. Although I was very young at the time, I did wonder how, if that was the case, it managed to hold any water. However later in life we had many happy weekends on the loch. Prior to our first trip, I purchased an Admiralty chart covering the entire area from Inverness to Loch Linnie, which is the sea loch that connects the Caledonian Canal to the Atlantic.

The chart showed that the greatest depth of the loch was just over 220 metres, and due to its surface area this made it the largest body of fresh water in the UK. The only other loch deeper than Loch Ness is Loch Morar, with a water depth of over 300 metres, which is the final loch in the Great Glen Fault before you descend the locks of the Caledonian Canal into the Atlantic.

During all of this time we never saw a monster, but I did not believe the monster existed. This is for the simple reason that the streams and rivers feeding Loch Ness contain a lot of peat. This gives the water in the loch the colour of tea, and very little light penetrates more than a few metres below the surface. Because of this, there is virtually no plant life in the loch, which is the basis of the food chain. There are, therefore, very few fish in Loch Ness and there is certainly not enough food to support a breeding colony of large top predators.

I believe that the legend of the Loch Ness monster is due to the winds and circulation patterns prevalent within the loch. As the prevailing winds in the UK come from the south-west, they tend to push the water up to the north-eastern end of the loch during periods when the wind is strong. When the wind eases, the surface water then moves back towards the south-west end of the loch, even if a small south-westerly wind is still blowing. If any surface debris, such as a floating tree, is observed from the shore, it will be caught in this counterbalancing current, and therefore appear to be moving against the direction of the wind. I think this is what led some people to believe that, as they were moving in the wrong direction, they must therefore be some type of creature.

The loch was extensively surveyed during the 1990s by many vessels deploying a curtain of the very latest technology in side-scanning sonar. These searches were carried out from one end of the loch to the other, but no monster has ever been found. However the monster legend makes a good deal of money for Scottish tourism.

Before moving on to Lake Toplitz, I remember that I was tripped up once in a pub quiz regarding a question on the largest freshwater lake in the world. I asked the quizmaster if he was referring to the lake with the largest volume of freshwater in the world, or the lake with the largest surface area. He replied that he did not know, and he was just there to read out the questions! I then decided that our team answer would be Lake Baikal.

Lake Baikal is a rift lake situated in the Russian region of Siberia. It has a surface area of around 32,000 square kilometres (less than that of Lake Superior), but it has an average water depth of nearly 750 metres, making it the largest body of unfrozen fresh water on the planet. Lake Baikal is also the world's oldest and deepest freshwater lake, and contains a volume of around 5,500 cubic miles of freshwater. I lost our team a point on that one, as the "correct" answer was Lake Superior.

Now we will move on to Lake Toplitz (Toplitzsee in German). This is a lake situated in a dense mountain forest high up in the Austrian Alps, 98 kilometres from Salzburg in western Austria. It is surrounded by cliffs and forests in a beautiful setting in the Salzkammergut lake district, within the Totes Gebirge (Dead Mountains).

The Toplitzsee water contains no oxygen below a depth of 20 metres. Fish can survive only in the top 18m, as the water below 20m is salty, although bacteria and worms have been found below 20m that can live without oxygen.

During 1943–44, the shore of Lake Toplitz served as a Nazi naval testing station. Using copper diaphragms, scientists experimented with different explosive types, detonating up to 4,000 kg charges at various depths. They also fired torpedoes from a launching pad in the lake into the Totes Mountains, producing vast holes in the canyon walls. The area is accessible only on foot by a mile-long path, as the K-Mautner-Weg is a private road that serves the Fisherman's Hut restaurant at the western end.

Lake Toplitz has inspired numerous expeditions causing several mysterious deaths. But seventy years after Nazi officers hid metal boxes in the depths of Lake Toplitz, a new attempt is being made to recover the Third Reich's fabled lost gold. The Austrian government has given a US team permission to make an underwater expedition to the log-infested bottom of the lake. Treasure hunters have been flocking to Lake Toplitz ever since a group of diehard Nazis retreated to this picturesque part of the Austrian Alps in the final months of World War II.

With US troops closing in and Germany on the brink of collapse, they transported the boxes to the edge of the lake, first by military vehicle and then by horse-drawn wagon, and sunk them. Nobody knows exactly what was inside. Some believe they contained gold looted by German troops throughout Europe and carried back to Germany. Others think that they contain documents showing where assets confiscated from Jewish victims were hidden in Swiss bank accounts.

The state company which controls the lake, Bundesforste AG, has signed contracts with several treasure hunters who hope to solve the mystery. Detailed underwater surveys of the 107 metre (350ft) deep lake followed, although there is profound official scepticism that there is anything left to find.

"I really don't know if there is anything down there, but we want to resolve the mystery once and for all," Irwin Klissenbauer, a director of Bundesforste AG, told the *Guardian*. "The aim at first is to map the lake floor."

He added: "This is a beautiful area. You have heard of Loch Ness. For Austrians this has been a bit like Loch Ness. Lots of people come here, and whether there is gold down there or not, the mystery has been very good for tourism." Mr Klissenbauer said that under the terms of the deals, any treasure found would be divided between the recovery teams and the Austrian state. He added, "Obviously if they recover anything which has an identifiable owner, under Austrian law we have to give it back."

This was not the first time explorers had tried to retrieve the lake's legendary lost gold. In 1947 a US Navy diver became entangled in Lake Toplitz's many submerged logs and drowned. Then in 1959 a team financed by the German magazine *Stern* had more luck, retrieving £72 million in forged sterling currency hidden in boxes, and also recovered the printing press. The currency, it turned out, was part of a secret counterfeiting operation, "Operation Bernhard", personally authorised by Adolf Hitler to weaken the British economy.

Over 100 million counterfeit pound sterling notes were said to have been dumped in the lake after Operation

Bernhard, which was never fully put into action. There is speculation that there might be other valuables to be recovered from the bottom of the Toplitzsee. The speculation is due to there being a layer of partly sunken logs suspended by a density boundary halfway to the bottom of the lake, making diving beyond it hazardous or impossible. Gerhard Zauner, one of the divers on the 1959 expedition, reports that he saw a sunken aircraft below this layer.

Nazis and Nazi sympathisers who had retreated to the Austrian Alps intending to fight a last-ditch guerrilla battle apparently dumped the currency to prevent its discovery. In 1963 the Austrian government imposed a temporary ban on explorations after another diver, led to the lake by an ex-SS officer, drowned during an illegal dive. More recent expeditions have had mixed fortunes. In 1983 a German biologist accidentally discovered more forged British pounds, numerous Nazi-era rockets and missiles that had crashed into the lake, as well as a previously unknown type of worm.

The last diving team to explore the lake, in 2000–01, had less luck. After a three-week search in an underwater diving capsule they came away with nothing more than a box full of beer caps, apparently dumped in the lake as a practical joke.

Mr Scott, whose previous expeditions have included a search in the Atlantic for a steamer carrying gold coins which sank on the way to Panama, said he was confident he would find "something damn big". "Until now nobody has explored the lake using hi-tech equipment. We will be the first people to go to the right spot," he told the Swiss news magazine *Facts*.

Mr Scott claimed to have discovered fresh clues in archives in both Berlin and Washington pointing him towards the gold, although he refused to give details. Some experts believe he may be right. They point out that the bottom of the lake is encrusted with a thick carpet of logs. Any treasure could be stuck in the mud underneath, they suggest.

"There is a lot of wood down there. We don't know yet whether it is possible to get through it," Mr Klissenbauer said. "You have to remember that the last lot who went down there with a mini U-boat didn't find anything." This attempt to pry loose the deep, dark secrets of Lake Toplitz and its legend of Nazi gold ended as mysteriously as it began.

More recently, a high-tech team from Oceaneering Technologies has combed the 100 metre deep, mile-long lake bed from end to end searching for "Nazi treasures", and has recovered "significant man-made objects", the search team said. Did the team have more than wads of old forged currency or a promising-looking box that turned out to contain nothing but old beer bottle caps and a note saying, "Sorry, not this time"? They would not say.

Ridge Albaugh, Oceaneering's project manager, said he located many new items, but was not specific about his finds. Albaugh earned his spurs exploring the *Titanic*, and diving to resolve the sad mystery of what happened to John F. Kennedy Jnr. when his plane plunged into the sea. His high-tech approach tells him, he says, that he now knows the bottom of that lake better than the back of his own hand.

However there were rumours that team members found boxes of old documents detailing property, cash and artefacts confiscated from mainly Jewish owners. The Simon Wiesenthal Centre in Los Angeles, the other backer of the project, is hoping for clues that will help Holocaust victims and their families get back all that stolen treasure.

I think the most intriguing part of the story of Lake Toplitz is that recovered Nazi documentation revealed that the Nazi Naval Research Centre performed a thorough survey of the lake prior to commencing operations there.

This 1942 survey recorded the deepest point as having a depth of just over 120 metres. Local farmers reported that after the Nazis had been observed dumping crates into the lake for many days, demolition crews drilled into the mountainside at this point, and the subsequent huge explosion brought down an entire section of the mountainside into the lake. Today the maximum surveyed depth of the lake is recorded as being 107 metres. Whatever was dumped in there by the Nazis now lies buried beneath some 13 metres of rock on the lake floor, and will almost certainly never be found.

We will now turn our attention to what is, in my opinion, the most fascinating and controversial lake that I have ever come across, namely Lake Vostok. Most people assume that Antarctica is too cold to hold any liquid water. This is not, in fact, the case. The region around the North Pole in the Arctic is merely frozen ice floating on the surface of the ocean, and it is not a landmass. Antarctica on the other hand is a continent, but due to its position surrounding the South Pole, it is permanently covered by up to four kilometres of ice.

However one of the major geological features of our planet is a huge rift zone that originates in Antarctica. It then runs under the Southern Ocean, into the Indian Ocean and makes landfall in East Africa. There it manifests itself as the East African Rift Valley, containing the Serengeti and Maasai Mari that we are all familiar with. This rift zone then continues from the Horn of Africa, northwards through the Red Sea, and then runs north through the Middle East. It finally stops on reaching the Zagros Fold and Thrust Belt, which geologically defines the eastern limit of the Persian Gulf oil fields.

Due to the geothermal heat created along this rift zone, rivers and lakes of liquid water are present on the rocky surface of Antarctica below the ice sheet. The liquid water in these features has been of great interest to scientists for many years, as the flora, forna and other biology that the systems contain will have evolved independently from other systems on the planet due to their complete isolation.

A number of incidents that have occurred over the years make Lake Vostok particularly intriguing. Firstly, the US military sent a naval task force there soon after World War II, the details of which remain classified to this day. Secondly there has been a lot of very unusual seismic activity around Lake Vostok that has been detected on seismographs around the world. The specific type of activity recorded should not occur in a geological area such as this.

Finally on 24th January 2001, all of the studies of Lake Vostok and the surrounding area were taken away from the US geological survey and NASA's JPL, and sole authority and control over all future investigations of the lake was given to the American National Security Agency (NSA). The NSA is the most covert department within the US secret service, even eclipsing the CIA. One wonders why this authority transfer took place, as the NSA are not the agency of choice to conduct a biological survey of a lake.

Lake Vostok is the largest of Antarctica's almost 400 known sub-glacial lakes. It was named after Russia's nearby Vostok Station, and lies under the surface of the central East Antarctic Ice Sheet, which is at 3,488 metres (11,444 feet) above mean sea level. The surface of this freshwater lake is approximately 4,000 metres (13,100 feet) under the surface of the ice, which places it at approximately 500 metres (1,600 feet) below sea level. Measuring 250 km long by 50 km wide at its widest point, and covering an area of 12,500 square kilometres, it contains an estimated volume of 5,400 cubic kilometres (1,300 cubic miles) of fresh water. The lake is divided into two deep basins by a ridge. The liquid water over the ridge has a depth of about 200 metres (700 feet), compared to roughly 400 metres (1,300 feet) of depth in the northern basin and 800 metres (2,600 feet) in the southern basin.

Studies of Lake Vostok have been undertaken by scientists from Russia, the USA, the UK, Germany and Japan at various times. The lake was drilled into by Russian scientists in 2012. The overlying ice provides a continuous paleo-climatic record of 400,000 years, although the lake water itself may have been isolated for up to twenty-five million years. On 5th February 2012, a team of Russian scientists claimed to have completed the longest ever ice core of 3,768 metres (12,400 feet), and pierced the ice shield to the surface of the lake. As soon as the ice was pierced, water from the underlying lake gushed up the borehole.

The first core of freshly frozen lake ice was obtained on 10th January 2013 at a depth of 3,406 metres (11,175 feet), and it is still being analysed. The Russian team plans to lower a probe into the lake to collect water samples and sediments from the lake bottom. It is hypothesised that unusual forms of life could be found in the lake's liquid layer, a fossil water reserve. Lake Vostok contains an environment that has been sealed off below the ice in conditions which could resemble those of the hypothesised ice-covered ocean of Jupiter's moon Europa.

The coldest temperature ever recorded on Earth (-89°C), was recorded at Vostok Station on 21st July 1983. The average water temperature of the lake is estimated to be just below 0°C. It remains liquid below the normal freezing point because of the high pressure caused by the weight of the ice above it. Geothermal heat from the Earth's interior is also available to warm the bottom of the lake. The ice sheet itself insulates the lake from cold temperatures on the surface.

German, Russian and Japanese researchers have also found that the lake has tides.

I find Lake Vostok so fascinating because sub-glacial lakes are completely different to anything that can be found at the Earth's surface. Although this lake is of a comparable size to some of the largest surface lakes on Earth, we know almost nothing about it. The fact that it could possibly hold ancient bacteria, or other forms of life, and provide scientists with information on possible life form evolvement on Europa and elsewhere is extremely exciting.

While researching this chapter, I have come across a lot of conspiracy theories regarding this lake. I believe that is because we know so little about it that some people's minds go into overdrive. The conspiracies that I have seen range from secret UFO bases to an underground city inhabited by the remains of the Third Reich. In my opinion, the first theory is 99.9 percent implausible, and the second theory completely implausible. However something unusual must be going on there because of the way that the authorities clam up when information is requested.

Firstly, it is a matter of public record that US Admiral Byrd led an expedition to Antarctica in 1946. This was not a scientific research expedition, but consisted of a flotilla of warships. I requested information on this subject under the Freedom of Information Act, but no information was forthcoming. In other words, whatever happened you're not about to find out about it any time soon.

Secondly, scientists today have a good understanding of the geology of the Antarctic continent. Some of the seismic activity recorded, and known to have originated in Antarctica, does not appear to have come from any normal geological processes. The intense, one-off and very short-lived spikes of P and S waves seen have nothing like the waveform or duration of earthquakes and other natural events. They resemble explosions as would be used in mining and tunnelling, but this type of activity is not supposed to be going on in Antarctica.

Finally, to the best of my knowledge, nobody has ever been given a rational explanation as to why the NSA should take over the US investigations of this lake. Lack of transparency on this point will only go to fuel further speculation regarding conspiracies, which is not good for the scientific community.

EPILOGUE

At the start of this book, the author asked that the reader set aside any preconceptions they may have regarding science and technology, and to examine the facts presented in the book with an open mind. I would like to think that having now read the book, the reader will be as fascinated by modern science as I am.

This book does not include a conclusions section as is normal, and it is left for the readers to draw their own conclusions regarding the many topics discussed. The information presented in this book comes from my discussions and meetings with many people, but mostly those in the scientific, military and industrial communities.

As we go through life, we meet many different people, and certainly my opinions on a variety of subjects have been profoundly changed and influenced through discussions with the people that I have encountered both on a professional and personal level.

I am now semi-retired, but still perform consulting work for various companies in the oil and gas industry. This work takes me to many countries, and I find that even at my age I am still learning all the time from the new people that I meet.

I am convinced that our knowledge of science will continue to expand at an exponential rate, and it will not be that long before we are actually travelling to the planets and, eventually, to the stars. It will certainly not happen in my lifetime, but for readers who are still in high school it may very well happen in yours.

The first manmade electricity was not generated until the 1830s. Within the next hundred years we had developed global electronic communications systems and national power grids, concepts that would not have even been thought of at that time.

Similarly, within less than a hundred years of the Wright brothers making their historic first flight of a few tens of metres, men were walking on the moon. Anyone who had suggested this possibility at that time would probably have been considered insane.

I hope that I have sparked an interest in physics and science in general among those who have read this book, and I sincerely hope that this book has maybe encouraged you to follow your dreams in life.

BACKGROUND

The inspiration to write this book came after reading the Stephen Hawking bestseller *A Brief History of Time*. The appeal of this book was such that it has sold over ten million copies worldwide. Stephen Hawking is a brilliant physicist, but nonetheless still a pure academic.

ABOUT THE BOOK

The book approaches the history of science and technology from a completely new angle. As the book progresses it becomes ever more intriguing, starting to explore the interaction between the giant industrial-military corporations and the intelligence-security services. These groups have effectively driven and funded modern science. A great amount of information in these areas is disclosed which has hitherto been unpublished. The book has now been completed with many illustrations. The author believes that no comparable or competing books have been published.

QUALIFICATION TO WRITE ON THIS SUBJECT

The author is an honours physics graduate, engineer and successful entrepreneur.

He has decades of experience interacting with global industrial groups and the intelligence-security services worldwide. In addition to presenting a history of science and technology, the book relates these experiences with a considerable amount of levity.

The author has had long conversations with many people, ranging from leading politicians, diplomats, billionaire heads of industry and security agents from many countries, to beggars, thieves and leaders of rogue nations. With few exceptions, he finds that you can learn a lot from most people if you take the time to listen to them.

The information presented in this book is factual. In cases where the information is inferred or taken from third party accounts this is stated. In some cases where the information presented comes from confidential sources or individuals who do not wish to be identified, their names have been changed.